SCENE OF CHANGE

SCENE
OF
CHANGE

A Lifetime in American Science

WARREN WEAVER

Charles Scribner's Sons · New York

To my wife, my son, and my daughter

The world's a scene of changes; and to be
Constant, in Nature were inconstancy.

Abraham Cowley, "Inconstancy"

Contents

Illustrations

1. Early Years

The population of Reedsburg, Wisconsin, in 1894 was something under two thousand persons. Whatever the exact number, it was increased by one on the early morning of July 17, for that is when and where I was born.

Southern Wisconsin was of course settled much later than was the Eastern seaboard, the first white family coming to the Reedsburg district from Green County, Ohio, in 1845. A Winnebago village was then located at the future site of Reedsburg, and indeed some Indian lodges remained until about 1915. My father was a druggist, and one of my earliest memories is of the blanket-wrapped Indians coming into my father's store to buy some gaudy trinket, or to sell him a ginseng root.

The local population was largely German, many settlers of that background having come to the locality in the 1850s and 1860s, characteristically arriving there, as did my forebears, as the third and often final stage of a journey which had originated in Europe and which had paused first in Pennsylvania and then in Ohio. A good deal of the business in my father's drug store was conducted in German.

It is difficult to recapture the sights, sounds, and smells of a Midwestern rural village of that period. It is still more difficult for the present-day reader, unless really elderly, to

1

imagine the nature of life at that time. The sidewalks were wooden, and there were then in Reedsburg no paved streets. We were untroubled by automobile traffic; over the two years just previous to my birth, J. Frank and Charles Duryea, back east in Springfield, Massachusetts, had been working on the design of the first gasoline-powered vehicle.

Neither town water nor household electricity was available at the time of my birth, although some houses were wired soon thereafter. Twenty telephones for business purposes (all on one line) were installed in 1887, but it was not until I was four years old that a general telephone company was organized for householders' service. That same year sewer drains were installed. A grade school of two rooms was built the year I was born, and a small community library was established just about the time I learned to read; the "Carnegie" library did not come until much later. There was no house-to-house mail delivery, although the first train had arrived from Chicago as long previously as January 1, 1872. The local farmers concentrated on potatoes, buckwheat, and hops—Pabst Blue Ribbon beer was first brewed at Milwaukee when I was one year old. The social life of the village centered primarily around the churches and the numerous fraternal lodges. The cartoonist Claire Briggs, who was born in Reedsburg, immortalized the local atmosphere, as a small boy knew it, in his well-known series on "The Ole Swimming Hole."

Indeed the world I was born into seems, from this distance, to have been a very simple and tranquil one. The front page of the weekly Reedsburg *Free Press* for Thursday, July 19, 1894 (there was no extra on the 17th!), was half-occupied with advertisements (Ladies Knit Vests, 5¢ each, good English currants, 3¢ per pound, Ladies Night

Robes, 65¢ to 95¢). The other three columns set forth the deliberations of the Common Council regarding the costs of installing a water works and an electric-light plant, and reported a local burglary ("the thieves escaped, but it was a lot of fun while it lasted"), and a county Republican meeting. There was a small story of the seemingly miraculous recovery of a woman from consumption, her life saved by "Dr. King's New Discovery," but the status of this entry is made somewhat dubious by its final words: "Free trial bottles at I. Weaver's Drug Store." Clearly this was a patent medicine, sold by my father.

It may not be surprising that this rural paper ran no state, national, or international news, but *The New York Times,* on the front page of July 17, 1894 (the issue was twelve pages long and cost three cents), also carried no headlines. Three of the seven columns have a somewhat current flavor, for they covered the resignation of the city police commissioner. Another full column dealt with the necessity to protect the price of sugar. A column and a half was devoted to an accident in Chicago. Dated from Rondout, New York, was the stirring front-page news that a number of members of the Gould family "came down the Ulster and Delaware from Roxbury this morning and took a Hudson River train for Tarrytown." There was not a single piece of international news on the entire front page.

It has become trite to speak of the almost dizzying rate at which life has recently been changing. Indeed, it must be soberly true that the Biblical span of three score years and ten has at no other time in history covered such profound changes as those experienced during my lifetime since 1894. I can just picture the bemused incredulity of my Grandmother Weaver, standing by the cookstove that was the sole source of heat for one end of her small house —on which stove, incidentally, was always standing a hospitable pot of coffee. And speaking of sources of heat, I recall the "register" in the floor of my bedroom. It was connected to no furnace, but was simply a hole through the floor that allowed some heat to leak up into my upstairs room from the room beneath in which was located a stove. Going to bed on a winter night involved a hurried minute of shivering undressing and of contact with the cold bed—followed by the smothering but welcome weight of blankets and "comforters."

Our meals consisted largely of bread, meat, potatoes, milk, homemade pickles and conserves, pies and cakes. Ice cream was a rarity, since it required bringing home a chunk of ice in a cart, packing the home freezer with a mixture of crushed ice and rock salt, and turning the stiff crank for some twenty minutes—but licking the dasher made all this worthwhile. Our food was entirely seasonal. Salads were items on feminine menus, but were disdained by menfolk. Bread cost five cents a loaf and milk four cents a quart. When I was sent to the butchershop there never was any charge for a soup bone, and liver and sweetbreads were free for the asking.

My father's drug store had, during the summer months, a soda fountain, and not only the ice cream but all the chocolate, vanilla, and fruit syrups were made on the premises. From October until late spring this fountain was covered over with a display counter on which, at Christmastime, was box after box of hideously overdecorated "dresser sets" of combs, brushes, mirrors, nail files, buffers, and the like, all in big cases, with satin-lined compartments. These were—ridiculously, pathetically, but rather touchingly—

a standard local way for the farmers to express devotion to their wives at Christmastime.

The facilities for entertainment in those pre-TV, pre-radio, pre-movie, and indeed pre-phonograph days were simple indeed. In the summer there might be a Chautauqua meeting or a circus, and the annual Sunday-school picnic at nearby Devil's Lake was a highlight of the year. There was an "Opera House" at which there were occasional "readings" and concerts. In the home there was likely to be one "family" magazine, a tiny library of well-worn books, a stereopticon viewer with slides of the Chicago World's Fair, and just possibly a small and rather primitive "Magic Lantern." One of the simple but attractive pleasures was the observance of May Day. One made fancy little colored paper baskets and hung them on friends' door knobs, especially favorite girl friends. Each basket was filled with violets, cowslips, or—in the case of a special favorite—the fragrant arbutus which was not common in our neighborhood, but which could be sought out.

One of my great-grandparents came from England and one from Holland, but all the rest, as far as I know, came from Strassburg when it was in German territory. My paternal great-grandfather, named Josiah Weber, was born aboard ship on the journey to America in 1791. His father, David Weber, had been a weaver of cloth. The name of his son, my great-grandfather, was automatically changed from Josiah Weber to Jesse Weaver when a lawyer in Wayne County, Ohio, where they had a farm, translated his German birth certificate. These were simple, solid folk, the devotion of my forebears to their Lutheran faith being reflected in the numerous Biblical names such as David, Josiah, Jacob, Moses, Abraham, and—the name of my father —Isaiah. My maternal grandfather, John Stupfell, one of the dearest and finest persons I have ever known, spent his life as a clerk in a country drygoods store. He was a devout and dedicated Christian, teaching Sunday school and being one of the small group of the faithful who always went to Wednesday-night prayer meeting. Both my maternal and my paternal grandparents lived in a small village named Sharon, about fifty miles southeast of Reedsburg.

It is strange that some persons, relatively near and dear, can die, and then rather soon fade out of one's every-day thoughts, whereas others die but never seem to disappear.

My maternal grandfather is definitely in this second category. Surely a week does not pass without my thinking of him with pleasure, deep affection, and often inspiration. He was fond of frequently repeating a whole series of wise or humorous remarks that came to be referred to in the family as "John's Sayings." To this day, if my wife asks me how I like some new dish that I consider only fairly good, the reply is bound to be, "Well, as Grandpa would say, I wouldn't sit up nights to eat it."

I have the warmest recollections of the lazy vacation days spent at his home. In the front yard was the inevitable hammock in which I read many of the childhood classics; later in my university days I would retreat there for more serious reading—one summer it was the works of two Frenchmen: *La Chance* by the mathematician Felix Borel (1871–1956) and the scientific essays of Henri Poincaré (1854–1912).

Across the street was the village blacksmith shop, with

the cheery clink of hammer on forge and the acrid smell of the burning hoofs when the hot shoe was fitted. In the rear of the house was Grandpa's lush garden, an outdoor toilet surrounded by hollyhocks, and the redolent barn where the family horse was kept. On a hot summer afternoon one was allowed to take from the pantry shelf a small bottle of black-cherry extract, carefully pour out one spoonful, add sugar and cold water from the well—and there was the pause that refreshes, *à la* 1900.

I would like to believe that in the fortuitous mixing of the two genes for two generations I received a goodly share from my Grandfather Stupfell. Two things I am pretty sure that I did inherit from him—a gay and unworried inability to spell, and a love for teaching. At the time of their golden-wedding anniversary he wrote out by hand an account of his life. I have just reread it, and have chuckled on almost every page over words such as "barbacue," "Vaginia," "rigular," "toobs," "schollars." When he was twenty-one years old, the authorities of a nearby district school asked Grandpa if he would teach in their school— and could he teach algebra (which he remarks "was a new thing for district schools at that time"). He would, and could, and did; and in his final estimate of the experience, he wrote, in words that warm my heart for him, "besides giving them satisfaction, I had a grand good time."

I am skeptical concerning the significance of the recollections I have of my childhood. Do I remember chiefly the bizarre or the unpleasant? Whole extensive segments of my early experiences have been completely forgotten; this is not a result of my present age, for these gaps in memory have existed for many years. Whereas my wife can recite the songs she learned in kindergarten, practically my sole memory of my grade-school education up to the age of ten consists of the smarting recollection of having been forced to stand in the corner of the room, facing the walls, because (I assume) I had been very naughty.

My earliest memory is of the darkened hush of our home when scarlet fever caused it to be quarantined. I was thin and sickly as a child, and indeed not vigorous as a boy or a youth. I caught everything that was going around, including diphtheria. Of almost an equally early vintage is my memory of being taken to the German Lutheran church and observing the pastor at communion service standing before the pulpit, raising the goblet, and proclaiming, "I drink for all of you!" My grandparents and great-grandparents were all of the Lutheran faith, being so devoted that every Sunday found them in church, even in the days when this meant a horse-and-buggy ride of many miles. Early in my life, however, we shifted over to the Presbyterian church—I think this may have been because the Lutheran services were at least partly in German, a language my mother never learned.

My mother was small, frail, and a person so utterly lovely in her sweet and unselfish character that she was adored by all her friends, not to mention her family. The hours of a country drug store were long, and I saw relatively little of my father during Reedsburg days, although I do recall his taking me often, a sleepy and thoroughly bored small boy, to sit through the tedium of the then characteristic Wednesday-evening prayer meeting. These were, to me then and surely to me now in retrospect, queer and pathetically small meetings at which every one sat silent until some person was moved to rise and offer either a prayer or a "testimonial." Otherwise one just sat there in solemn and embarrassed silence: at least I was always embarrassed.

Occasionally I would be allowed to go to my father's drug store. Each late spring a traveling vendor set up shop in one of the front-window spaces and manufactured and sold "cotton candy" to the great delight of all the youngsters. The lower walls of the store were lined with tiers of small drawers. I remember the location and contents of only two, one of which contained sparkling strings of rock candy and the other redolent sticks, packed in aromatic bay leaves, of Spanish licorice.

Other forms of advertising not having been yet developed, companies would, from time to time, provide my father with a supply of handbills and free samples. One of my first adventures at earning money involved the house-to-house distribution of these samples at the rate of two cents per ten items. This earning was important to me, for although my parents were both generous and kind, my brother and I never received any allowance until our university days. Furthermore it was not part of the rather strict system of our family to ask for either money or presents. You merely hinted and hoped.

Fourth of July is also associated in my mind with my father's store. That day, in those times, was awaited with almost intolerable longing during the preceding two or three weeks when one saved his pennies, bought fireworks, and each day counted his accumulating hoard. On the day itself one lived a discontinuous sort of life. Up at dawn, there was a noisy period of shooting off firecrackers and bursting torpedoes, this almost never lasting until breakfast. I can this moment recall the acrid smell of the burnt powder and the musty odor of the punk we used as tinder: we all believed that this punk was made of camel dung.

Following the early morning spree there were hours of hot waiting, of almost intolerable suspense, until darkness finally settled down and the red fire, flower pots, pinwheels, Roman candles, and sky rockets could be fired off. My father's store was directly across Main Street from the one other competing drug store. About nine o'clock on the night of the Fourth, the devotees of each establishment began to shoot the larger Roman candles and rockets, not into the sky, but horizontally across the street at the rival store. Worse than that, eight-, ten-, and twelve-inch cannon crackers were lighted and thrown. We were a quiet little rural community, but we had our moments.

July brings another specially poignant memory, associated with my birthday. I do not recall ever having had a party to which children were invited, but there was always an evening family picnic on that day. My father for several years provided, as the climax to the evening, a tissue-paper balloon. I remember these as large, but I suspect they were actually not more than three or four feet in diameter when inflated. At the bottom was a light wooden ring with wires across it, suspending in the center of the ring a small wad that one soaked with kerosene. Then, with all the family holding out the tissue of the balloon so as to avoid a premature calamity, the kerosene was lighted and the hot rising air filled out the tissue balloon and it was ready to ascend. Released, it slowly and beautifully drifted off into the evening dusk, a bright symbol that a year was floating away. No member of the family ever said, "This is beautiful or symbolic": but I knew it was. It was *my birthday*. That lovely spot of light going off for an adventure in the sky was *my balloon.* I always watched until it had completely disappeared, and then I knew that a whole long year would have to pass before this would happen again. I was deeply moved by this recurrent ceremony, solemn and at the same time joyous, and I still recall it as one of the lovely—actually one of the few truly lovely—experiences of my childhood.

For me, childhood was not a happy time. I had few companions, and no really close friend. My brother, the only other child of the family, was five years older than I. That span of years is an unbridgeable gap when one is young, and my brother and I, while not at all enemies, simply were not friends in the sense of being playmates. Indeed I did not get to know my brother until late in my university days, and then discovered to my joy that he was a wonderful person. But as a child he was fat, boisterous, and had such a bad temper that I simply avoided him—not always successfully, to be sure, for I still carry high on my forehead a faint scar caused by a cut from a splint waste-paper basket that he kicked at me!

I had one boy companion of my own age, but the truth is that I considered him pretty stupid and uninteresting. He's dead now, and won't mind my saying this, and in retrospect I am sure I was correct. He was forever wanting to play with me, but I preferred to be alone. Two doors from us was a girl of about my age, with whom I played occasionally. I think she was not considered by my family as a wholly suitable companion, but she was sweet and kind to me at a period when this meant a great deal; and across the years, I thank her. Also nearby was the daughter of another family of German origin. I used to go to see her late on Saturday mornings, but primarily, I must confess, because her mother often made cream puffs on that day.

I was shy, introspective, not vigorous, and unskilled in the active games of childhood. I had big ears and a big nose, and fully realized that I was not physically attractive. I was uncomfortable a great deal of the time, in a world within which I really didn't know how to behave. I was often lonesome, and most of my memories of playing are of playing alone.

I have clear recollections of a number of isolated retreats where I used to go. There was a small elm in front of our house which was a poor climbing tree, but I could manage it; and the fact that it had room for only one person was a real asset. I wanted to get up off the ground where all the confusing adult things were happening, and construct a small protected world of my own where I could be quiet and undisturbed.

There was a dirt bank not far from our house, and I worked alone many secret hours there, making a shallow cave. Best of all was the storeroom of our home. There were open rafters above this room, and I could climb up and have a private place there all by myself. I am aware of the fact that a modern analyst would at once recognize the womblike character of all these restricted places, and whatever the implication, he would doubtless be right.

Even in those days a drug store carried a wide variety of items, and at Christmastime my father's store was filled with toys. For this he made a buying trip to Chicago each fall, and it was a family tradition that on his return he would bring a present to my brother and me. On one occasion it was the first pair of roller skates we had ever seen, and I remember this particularly vividly because my rather tubby brother first tried his skates on our small front porch, fell heavily on his substantial behind, and crashed right through the flooring.

My present from one of these Chicago trips was a one-dollar Ajax electric motor and a dry cell to run it. I was overjoyed. Within a week I had built from spools and suchlike all the little rotating devices which the tiny torque of the motor could manage. Then I began to penetrate its mysteries. First I took off the little bronze spring brushes to clean them. Then I took off the winding of the field coil and carefully replaced it. Finally, as a great triumph, I took off the more complicated armature windings, put them back on and—miracle—the motor would still run! I decided then and there that I wanted to spend my life building motors. I had no idea what you called persons who did this. I suspect that the word "science" was exceedingly little used in that village at that time, but some adult, sensing my enthusiasm, remarked that I would probably grow up to be an engineer. I at once completely adopted that word and idea, and through my grade school and high school years there never was the slightest doubt what I wanted to do. I wanted to be an engineer.

In these days of toy pistols and guns, perhaps we underestimate the importance of toys. Of all the toys I ever had, I remember especially three: this Ajax motor, a gyroscope bought at the Louisiana Purchase Exhibition at St. Louis in 1904, and a marvelous little device that drew complicated and beautiful curves, given me by my brother one year for Christmas.

My family, German in its basic traditions, was devoted to music. My father had a really good tenor voice, and loved to sing, in quartets or alone at home with my brother as accompanist. When I was very young—it must have been at least as early as age six—a small violin was purchased for me and I started taking lessons from a formidable female whose martinet ways and the musty smell of whose sealed-up house and stiff Victorian costumes I can still vividly recall. I disliked her and feared her, and when we moved to Madison I abandoned the violin and shifted to the cello.

In university days I dropped that instrument, concluding that my playing of it was an unjustified bit of selfishness—I liked doing it, but the result was not good enough to be generally acceptable.

This decision indirectly reminds me of a lifelong curiosity I have had about the magnitude of the range of "goodness" possible to various objects or procedures. For example there are some things (I would offer cheese, whisky, movies, and peanut butter as excellent instances) of which I consider that *all* examples are good. Some, to be sure, are better than others, and the best can be superb; but none is unacceptably bad.

On the other hand there are interesting objects or procedures which range over a spectacular spectrum of goodness, ranging all the way from unspeakably bad to almost indescribably good. They maximize, as a mathematician would say, the ratio of the goodness of the best examples to the badness of the worst. In this category I would, for instance, place martinis. I had one once in a hotel in Delhi which was without question the worst drink I have ever tasted. But as made by our gifted next-door neighbor in Connecticut, dry martinis can be as far out in the ultraviolet of excellence as the Delhi one was deep in the infrared. These parenthetic remarks are stimulated by the mention, just above, of violin playing. For I think this the ultimate illustration of a procedure with the maximum range from worst to best. I am unable to think of anything more heavenly at its best and more punishing and terrible at its worst.

My father was an ambitious and a restless man, and after years of long hours in his drug store in Reedsburg, he decided to shift to a larger scene. Accordingly in 1904, when I was ten, the family moved to Madison, the capital city of the state of Wisconsin. This move was made simultaneously with a trip to the International Exhibition at St. Louis. Up to that time a summer visit to my grandparents had been the limit of my travel, and the World's Fair of 1904 was an exciting adventure indeed.

Not long after we moved to Wisconsin's capital city my mother, never vigorous, became very ill. She was taken to a hospital in Chicago, I assume with the desperate hope of an operation. From what little I know of the sad business, I conclude that she probably had cancer of the stomach. I recall the tense fear of the moment when my father told me that things were worse—that he and I would have to go to Chicago. We knelt together on the floor to say a prayer, and started sadly off. Within a few days my mother was dead.

She was buried in Sharon, the home of my grandparents, and the circumstances and atmosphere of the funeral are still fresh in my mind, more as a vulgar and inexcusable affair than as a sad affair.

I then held instinctively what I now hold as a deep conviction, that so-called Christian burial is often a savage and cruel procedure. Fortunately, I was allowed to absent myself from the awful ceremony, and for an hour or more

sat up in one of the apple trees in the rear of my grandfather's yard, thinking about how lovely and dear my
mother had been.

There is little of my grade-school and high-school years
that is of enough general interest to be worth recording.
I continued to be socially inept, having a fierce envy of
those who always seemed to know just what to do and what
to say. The transition from a relatively small and familiar
grade school to a large and strange high school was a difficult one for me. On the day of graduation from eighth
grade I went at once to my father's store, found an isolated
place at the back, and cried bitterly, both because of what
I was facing and because of what I was leaving behind. No
later school transition was even approximately as moving
to me.

I did, however, have the great good fortune to make
two true friends. Two doors from our house was the gay,
elegant, and talented Brant family, with four sons. One of
these, Selwyn, was my age. He had manners, dash, and
grace; he was brilliant and witty. For reasons I did not
understand but was thankful for, he accepted me. We
played together at all sorts of imaginative games. We sol-
emnly decided that we would collaborate on the world's
best book on arms and armor. We worked together on a
little neighborhood sheet called "Wit and Humor" for
which I furnished the drawings. We were close companions
all through grade school and high school. There was a lapse
in our relationship during college days (when I was a grind
and he a swell), and then we drifted apart for many years.

But now, after all these years, he is again my great and **dear** friend.

The other friend was of a different but equally fine sort. Richard N. Hunt was the son of our beloved family minister. Dick was studious, solid, dependable, loyal. No more social than I was, we made all sorts of things in his basement (he had good tools, which I lacked), and went on pre-breakfast birding trips on our bicycles. My friendship with Dick, begun during high school, has ripened and deepened with every year that has passed. He has had a very distinguished career as a mining geologist, and is the closest nonfamily friend I have ever had.

Do not get the impression that I was always morose and troubled. I hugely enjoyed then, as I still do, the surge of the seasons—the wonderful first warm days of spring when freshets in the gutters made it possible to race small drifting "boats," the lazy summer evenings all lit up with fireflies, the crisp cold of winter. I am convinced the planet has warmed up since then, for I remember a solid week in Madison when it never got above minus ten, and walks to school in Great Falls, Montana (where we lived for a brief period while I was in high school), across a stretch of open prairie with the thermometer at forty below.

I loved reading, and ran a regular monthly bill at the public library for keeping books overtime. There is nothing quite like the anguished sweetness, the almost exquisite agony, of nearing the end of a wonderful childhood book. I devoured all the classic fairy stories, preparing the way for my adult love of *The Wind in the Willows, Winnie-the-Pooh,* and of course *Alice in Wonderland.*

As I have said, I had at least two real friends, but I

was never a part of an active social circle. I did not dance or go to parties. In high school I observed from an embarrassed distance the popular ones who always had the quick and easy remark, whose two-inch-high collars met just so in the latest style. As I look back over the years and remember what has happened to many of them I realize how misplaced was my admiration and envy. But I must in all honesty say that I was neither very comfortable nor very happy during those years.

I have no doubt that I was a difficult and irritating child. My relation with my father, which was seldom a very relaxed one, was poisoned by periods in which I would retreat into silence, sulking because I thought I had been misjudged, punishing my father for behavior on his part that I considered ill-advised or unfair. I do not think any of these experiences especially unusual, for I strongly suspect that childhood is often, and perhaps even characteristically, a troubled and unhappy time.

There is moreover no slightest element of self-pity involved in my saying all this, and I should make clear why I am emphasizing the restricted character of my youngest years. I state all this so that I can the more strongly contrast the rest of the story. Even during many of my college days I was restless, unsatisfied, and often lonely. But just about then the tide turned. I began to be engaged in efforts that were really rewarding. I tried things that I could do well. I began to acquire confidence and to be at ease. I began to be really happy. By the time I was fifty I had actually reached the point of no longer being awed by waiters!

From college days on—for the whole of the half century since then—the curve of life has, for me, gone steadily upward. As I hope will be evident from all I say about the years following college, life has become progressively richer, gayer, and happier with every succeeding year. I want no one to feel sorry about my childhood. As a preparation, it was well worth going through.

My grade-school teachers in Madison were excellent, and when I entered seventh grade I promptly fell in love with my teacher, Miss Kavanaugh. She was a strict disciplinarian, but when we deserved it she rewarded us with all sorts of special experiences. We learned, and recited in unison with great gusto, *"Spartacus to the Gladiators,"* and whole passages of *The Lady of the Lake*. Every one in the class respected and liked her, and I adored her.

Indeed my reports home were so glowing that my lonesome widowed father decided to visit the seventh grade at Washington School to see how much I had exaggerated. He must have concluded that for once I was right, for midway in my high-school years he married her. By this time my father had sold his store, and was experimenting in buying and selling Western land; and in the fall of 1910, just after the marriage, we moved, for a strange Western interlude lasting only a little more than a year, to Great Falls, Montana. We then returned to Madison.

The Western episode floats in my memory almost as unreal as a dream. There were wonderful fishing days in mountain streams, and equally wonderful fall hunting of prairie chicken in endless fields of wheat stubble. I had a remarkable male Latin teacher who taught us how to scan Vergil so that, reading aloud, we realized that we were not merely learning a foreign language but were learning to know a great poet. I summoned up my courage to take part in a "declamation contest" and won it with a talk (not quite extemporaneous: we were given ten minutes to prepare) on Robert Marion La Follette. Later, at the state contest at Bozeman, I was soundly beaten by a chap, some ten years older, who had had very practical oratorical training as a side-show barker with a circus.

To return to my newly acquired stepmother, Cicely Ann Kavanaugh Weaver was for so much of my life my understanding parent that I almost completely forgot that she was my stepmother. When she wrote her will, late in her life, she had a real row with the lawyer, for the relationship between us had become so close that she refused to refer to me as her stepson. She was a most remarkable and dear person, fierce and irrational in her loyalties, painfully sensitive in her pride and her determination to exclude the world from her private affairs, and with an excellent and restless mind. In many ways she did more for me than my own mother could have done. I loved her dearly, and we were exceedingly devoted to each other.

I achieved with her a relationship that I never approximated in the case of my father. The last ten or fifteen years of his life could hardly have been very rewarding to him. He was restless without a regular occupation, too energetic to loaf, and indeed not well enough off financially to retire so young. He bought still another drug store, but soon sold it. To my deep disappointment and confusion, he became less interested in the church. Throughout my life he was always addressed as "Father," spelled, I would suppose, with a capital letter. In happy contrast, my children and grandchildren call me everything from "Dad" to "Hi there." The only close tie I had with my father was the outdoors.

He loved to hunt and fish, as I did also, and as my physically less active and artistic brother Paul did not; so we had on trout streams, in the autumn woods, and over the fall duck blinds, the happy hours together that I most prize to remember.

My father, although he had the characteristic German love of music and as a young man was first tenor in the principal Reedsburg quartet, was primarily interested in business. From early days he had been reconciled to my becoming an "engineer"; but he was determined that my brother become a banker, which he thought of as the highest rung in the business ladder. My poor brother had to take, in the university, all sorts of courses in economics, money and banking, accounting, and the like. All of these he loathed; his only interest, and clearly his outstanding talent, was in music. Indeed he spent over a year behind a window in a bank before he rebelled (what tense family meals we had during that period!) and went back to the university on his own to study harmony, counterpoint, piano, organ. After a few years of preliminary struggle he became head of the Department of Music at the University of North Carolina at Chapel Hill, and then, for some ten years before his death in 1946 at the age of only fifty-seven, head of the School of Music at Cornell. He was a superb pianist and organist, and a successful trainer and leader of choral groups. Having all through childhood and boyhood been completely blocked off from him because he was my older brother, I became acquainted with him late in university days; and from then on we were close and devoted friends.

Although I had good teachers in Madison Central High School, none really compared with my Vergil teacher in

Great Falls, or with one or two I was to have in the university. I did, however, have a specially good time in physics. The young teacher (later to become City Superintendent of Schools) let me help him in the laboratory and with setting up his lecture experiments. At that time I started the career—not yet terminated—of making radio sets. The first one—I suppose about 1909—was a typical Marconi coherer set, with which I could hear a signal from the two-inch spark coil that the physics teacher operated in the high-school physics laboratory, located in the same square block our house was in. I gradually advanced to a molybdenum or silicon crystal set (the hours of exploring its surface with the "cat whisker" to find the most sensitive spot!), and then as a great advance, a set with an electrolytic detector—a silver-and-platinum Wolliston wire just touching the surface of a drop of acid resting in a little carbon cup. This was eventually replaced by a vacuum tube detector run on a storage battery. Finally, as almost a miracle, came the first "loud-speaker," and over the years, as my small resources increased, I built larger and larger sets. By the time our son was born, in 1923, I had a multiple-tube superheterodyne with which, when I got up at 2 A.M. to warm his milk, I could sometimes—just barely—hear the West Coast stations. The last of this long series, to finish off this topic, is an eight-channel sixteen-transistor all-wave set built only last year, from which, the first time it was ever turned on (in our present hilltop home in Connecticut), there emerged strange sounds that proved to come from a station in Algiers. From the spark coil across the block, through the Morse code from the Great Lakes steamers, to the world-wide short-wave signals on a portable solid-state multiple-channel set!

My minor adventures with physics illustrate the fact that high-school days were by no means uniformly dark ones. We had an attractive young teacher of English and speech who organized and directed student plays. My senior year the school put on *The Merchant of Venice,* and I played Bassanio—atrociously, I am sure, but with great satisfaction to me. The performance as a whole was good enough so that several years later the cast was reassembled for repeat performances that even involved a trip to two small neighboring towns. That was fun indeed.

As high school was drawing to a close the question of my university course became a pressing one. I would of course register as an engineer, but by that time I had learned that there were varieties of engineering. My father took me to see a local civil engineer (a church friend) for advice. He asked, "Do you want to spend your life working for some big company, or would you like to look forward eventually to being your own boss?" The answer to that was obvious, so he said, "Then you should train to be a civil engineer." That settled that.

2. College

Because my family lived in Madison, Wisconsin, and residents of the state paid no tuition, it was a foregone conclusion that I would attend the University of Wisconsin. Great as is my respect and affection for that institution, I regret in some ways that automatic decision, for it left me living at home when I badly needed being dumped out into the world. Although my older and more socially talented brother was asked to join a fraternity his freshman year, this was not repeated in my case. I felt crushed. Later I did join a fraternity, but I was not active in its social program. In retrospect I consider the whole fraternity business a completely silly one, nearly useless to those who are selected, and often cruel to those who are not. The institution is most strongly and clearly condemned by the characteristics of those who defend it.

But at home, and with almost no competing attractions, I worked hard. As soon as I had established a university record, I was permitted to elect a heavy schedule—seventeen to twenty-one credits a semester. Early in my sophomore year I began to sense the semantic error that had previously equated the words "engineering" and "science." I do not mean to imply that I did not appreciate and enjoy the strictly engineering subjects, for I did. In those days one could enroll at Wisconsin for a five-year course that earned a professional degree—in my case that of C. E.—and I stuck out the whole five years and have never for a moment regretted that I did so, even though I have never explicitly made use of this civil engineering training.

The awakening occurred during the first semester of my second year when, according to the now outdated system then in use, my sophomore mathematics subject was differential calculus. Not only did I then for the first time meet a really poetic branch of mathematics, all alive with excitement and power and logical beauty—I had the great good fortune to have a truly great teacher.

Charles Sumner Slichter, applied mathematician, chairman of the department in my student days and dean of the graduate school in my early teaching days, was a towering figure of a man. He deserves a whole book, and I understand one is presently to be written. He was a Renaissance man, physically vigorous, penetrating in his thought and comments, handsome with his great mane of iron-gray hair, explosive alike in his humor and his disdain for the dull and commonplace, full of zest for the whole of life. If he had been born in the seventeenth century he would have been one of the leaders in the formation of the Royal Society Club of England, a lively and fully participating member of the group that met at the Boar's Head Tavern to drink ale, eat thirteen courses, and argue all night about science, philosophy, art, and life.

To have him as an undergraduate teacher of calculus was a truly marvelous experience. The high-school mathematics of my period was on the whole a pretty dull business, but calculus, with its graceful and profound capacity for dealing with change, was something strikingly new and exciting. From my point of view Slichter was an absolutely ideal teacher, certainly the greatest I ever had. He was careless, even contemptuous, about unimportant details; but the dramatic power of the analytic tools of mathematics to explore natural phenomena was spread before us by him as it could have been by Newton himself. I must admit that he both confused and frightened some of the poorer students. I recall an earnest boy who asked the professor a stupid question. Slichter paused for several ominous seconds, and then with unexpected calm said, "Bill, suppose you stay after class and ask the janitor."

Over the years in which I took course after course with Slichter, my respect, admiration—and eventually affection —for him steadily grew. Of his four distinguished sons, the scientist son, Louis Byrne Slichter, one of our country's leading geophysicists, had been an earlier acquaintance and became my friend in university days. He has over all the intervening years grown to be one of my very closest friends.

Following his most active teaching period, Slichter was an imaginative, if admittedly unorthodox, dean of the graduate school. In his office one day, he called me to his desk and said with evident glee, "Here's a chap I am certainly going to let into the graduate school. Look at his transcript! See what judgment he used in picking courses to flunk in!" I get a particular charge out of this story as I look at my eighth-grade report card, which lists 98 in drawing, 97 in algebra, English, and music—but a very low mark in both spelling and deportment.

Professor Slichter was my scientific godfather. Whenever a critical moment arose as my program developed, he was influential, wise, and sympathetically on my side. When his colleagues wanted a portrait of him painted, the dean characteristically refused to sit for hours (I can imagine him saying "like a dummy"), but a fine artist was located who agreed to work on the basis of one sitting at which he would make a pencil portait sketch, plus one other short session at which the artist would make only a palette of tints and colors of skin, eyes, hair. The pencil portrait turned out to be superb, and Slichter had a few copies made of it. He had, in fact, five made, for his four sons and for me. Very few things in my life have given me the satisfaction I had when the dean handed me my copy and remarked, "I had one made for each of my boys."

I had other splendid undergraduate teachers, notably Arnold Dresden, who later had a long career at Swarthmore. He was a real scholar, a gifted linguist, and an able and enthusiastic musician. He was a bearded sophisticated gentleman of European background, and I was as yet not fully emerged from Reedsburg; but he invited me to his home, and thrilled me by insisting that as friends we should use first names. Life was indeed beginning to open up new and happier horizons.

I had my first really tough mathematics subject under Dresden—theory of functions of a real variable. By my junior year I clearly realized that I was going to go on with advanced mathematical training, and I devoted all the slack in my schedule to electives in that department. So in my fifth year, still technically an undergraduate engineer, I was in Arnold Dresden's class, exposed to the initially bewildering abstractions of the theory, developed by the German mathematician Georg Cantor (1845–1918), which placed the definition of irrational numbers on a strictly logical basis. It almost killed me, it seemed so strange and difficult; but I loved it, spent hours and hours on every lecture and, in the modern idiom, was hooked.

I had one other truly great teacher, who went on to develop into an even closer friend and long-time associate than did Slichter. That was Max Mason (1877–1961), then the top theoreticist of the University of Wisconsin's physics department, and indeed one of the recognized intellectual leaders of the American community.

My five-year undergraduate course gave me a chance to do a substantial amount of normally graduate work before I took my first degree; and the one most influential course I took was electrodynamic theory under Mason.

Remember that this was over a half century ago. The joining up had only recently occurred of the compact and powerful analytical formulation of the electromagnetic field theory of the English physicist James Clerk Maxwell (1831–1879) with the more modern and truly exciting electron theory of the Dutch physicist Hendrik Antoon Lorentz (1853–1928). Mason had an analytical power and dexterity that was as precise, graceful, and effective as was his skill with a billiard cue. His lectures were difficult, demanding, brilliant, and hugely stimulating. He opened up a whole new world for me. When I first walked into his class I unsuspectingly took a turning that profoundly affected all the rest of my life.

Mason as a teacher preserved a delicate balance between the vigor, drama, and robustness of Slichter and the precision and erudition of Dresden. His courses were difficult for the better students and must have been a nightmare for a conscientious poor student. He had little respect for the routinely methodical teachers who lectured in so finished (and dull) a manner that the student took away from the course "a notebook," as he himself once wrote in a letter, "that was almost as good as a two-dollar textbook." His command of formal mathematical technique was powerful and effortless. He could be exquisitely precise, but he could also accomplish imaginative leaps around or over difficulties. He had a great and lasting influence on a large number of graduate students. The mediocre ones found him pretty tough, but the really good ones almost worshipped him.

I think there can be no doubt that Max Mason's greatest talent was his outstanding capacity as a teacher. The warmth of his personality, the delightful play of his humor, the swift and smooth working of his mind—all these were combined in the most effective way both in his formal lectures (which were never formal) and in his very extensive personal work with graduate students. A large number of persons, including some of today's most distinguished North American scientists, look back on their association with Max as, with no possible doubt, the high point of their student life.

He had had the best possible preparation for his teaching. It was Slichter who in undergraduate courses first stimulated Mason's interest in mathematics, and in September 1900 he went to Göttingen, at that time the leading mathematics center of the world, and began the study and research that led to the Ph.D degree, *magna cum laude*, in May 1903. During the Göttingen days there fully emerged the almost incredible combination of charm, gaiety, versatility, and brilliance that characterized all of his adult life. He loved the student life in Germany, and he could handle even the German language with the same relaxed dexterity he demonstrated with advanced mathematics.

He wrote his doctoral dissertation under the famous German mathematician David Hilbert (1862–1943). This renowned scholar assigned him a thesis problem, and in a short time Mason reported with a complete and elegant solution, his method being so powerful that the entire exposition required only a couple of pages.

Hilbert congratulated him but explained that two pages could not constitute a doctoral dissertation at Göttingen. A new subject was assigned, and, not surprisingly, this one proved to be very difficult. In fact, after Mason had spent several months in an unsuccessful assault, Hilbert suggested changing once again to a new topic. Then one night Mason awoke about 3 A.M. with the whole solution clear in his mind. He got out of bed and wrote steadily for two hours. In the morning, when he examined the compact notes, everything was sound and in order. Hilbert was surprised and highly pleased with the solution, and Mason, as he himself reported the episode, "didn't have the courage to tell him that I had, in fact, dreamed the solution." Mason never had another experience of this sort.

It is my own prejudiced judgment that Max Mason should have continued to be a teacher and a scientist. His public recognition as a research expert would probably have been restricted in large part to those who knew him, for he was almost totally uninterested in publication. In a four-year period at Yale, after taking his degree, he did write a group of eight brilliant papers, on boundary value problems, differential equations, and calculus of variations. But these were the only mathematical papers he published. His mind moved so much faster than his pencil that he found it disagreeable to write down almost anything other than very fragmentary notes—often so illegible that he himself could not read them after they cooled off. He had, in fact, an almost pathological dislike of writing, and this, combined with his exceedingly high standards and his disdain for what he viewed to be trivial work, is responsible for the fact that his record of publication bears no discernible relation to his capacities or, indeed, to his actual output. Time after time he would produce a brilliant and elegantly compact solution of a problem. All his colleagues who knew about the work would urge him to publish. But this involved the, to him, dull drudgery of writing out something that his mind had left far behind.

During his years at Wisconsin, Mason was viewed as a leading member of the faculty, one of the university's best scholars and most brilliant minds. He was very popular with both faculty and students.

Mason left the University of Wisconsin to become, in October 1925, President of the University of Chicago. He held this position for less than three years, after which he joined the staff on the Rockefeller Foundation, first being in charge of all their work in the natural sciences and then, for six more years, being its president. His name will recur in these pages, since he was a working companion of mine for some sixteen years.

Max was not a great administrator. His mercurial brilliance was such that systematic preparation for meetings and sustained study of proposals submitted to him were simply not congenial to him. When he had an important speech to make, he took a mischievous (and to his colleagues exasperating) pleasure in refusing to prepare for the occasion, preferring to speak extemporaneously. He was a multiply talented man. In fact, I simply do not know anything which, being seriously attempted, he did not do exceedingly well. He was, in his youth, a champion high jumper. He was for a time the unofficial golf champion of Wisconsin. He was an excellent bridge player and a highly skilled billiard player. During all his life Max had a devastating dislike of the superficial and an incredible capacity to penetrate with lightning speed to the significant core of any problem. On one of his trips to Paris he bought what he always referred to as "a hand-painted picture." Part of this picture he disliked, so he bought a kit of oil paints and proceeded, never having had the slightest previous experience, to repaint the unsatisfactory parts. Not only did he proceed, he succeeded very well indeed.

Max did not suffer fools gladly, and he was distinguished for his enemies as well as for his friends. He was brilliantly witty, but on occasion the wit could be caustic. Such superlatives should be used responsibly, so I must make clear that it is the growing judgment reached over many years that places Max's as the most powerful and penetrating mind I have ever known. It has been one of the greatest privileges of my life that for so many years we were working colleagues and ever closer and closer friends.

The civil engineers of those days at Wisconsin had to take a summer field course in surveying, this being given in idyllic surroundings at Devil's Lake, near Baraboo. I took this course the summer of my sophomore year, and during both my third and fourth summers I attended again as a teaching assistant, being responsible for the course in those aspects of observational astronomy that might be useful to a civil engineer—determination of latitude and longitude, of true north, and so on. This was a germinal experience. I discovered that teaching was even more fun than learning. I discovered that, in spite of my contemporary age and my limitations in many directions, I could as a teacher command the interest and respect of my companions. In those days almost anyone interested in science took for granted that he would be a teacher, for full-time research positions were then almost nonexistent; but from that time forward I was headed for teaching not by default, but as an enthusiastic choice.

In the late spring of 1916, prior to the fifth year of the course which led to the professional degree of civil engineer, I applied for a scholarship. It turned out that one of the conditions required the applicant to have a bachelor of science degree. I had left for summer teaching at Devil's Lake before I knew of that requirement, and to this day I am not certain whether the authorities waived the requirement or granted me a B.S. in absentia that June; but in any event I received the scholarship.

The last semester of my five-year course, in the spring of 1917, was upset by the excitement over the war. The actual declaration came on April 6, and on June 5 registration for national service took place. An ardent pacifist in times of peace, I was nevertheless thoroughly determined to get into the thick of World War I. But I was too thin to get into the thick of it. I tried all sorts of inconvenient and unpleasant methods of adding to my weight, including eating more bananas than I like to remember, in preparation for a Navy physical. I simply could not meet the requirements for regular enlistment. It was the spring of 1918 before I managed to get into uniform.

I emerged from the university, as could not have been

visible to the eye, a very different person from the still rather moody and shy freshman who entered. I had found something that I could do well, and I had a junior Tau Beta Pi membership to prove it (an honorary fraternity, as I always insist to my Phi Beta Kappa wife, son, and daughter, that *really* has scholastic standards). I was standing on my own feet. In high school it was faintly disgraceful to get high marks, and it certainly gave one no general standing; but in university this was not the case. I was beginning to have enough confidence to be a little relaxed in my relationships with others. Having no job and no money, I nevertheless began to have some security. I was looking forward eagerly to getting a real job.

These reasons, important as they were, are only a small part of the story of my emergence into a happy life. For something else had happened that was to bring me joy and inspiration in ever-increasing measure all the rest of my life. I fell in love.

I cannot understand persons who write about their lives but do not so much as mention wife and children. To be sure, that is a private sort of subject, which can easily be boring and inappropriate. But it is impossible for me to leave out Mary—or my son and daughter. I will get it over with promptly, and the reader must then realize that they are silently behind any good or happy incident that comes up later.

I had had crushes—innocent and usually of brief duration—previous to meeting Mary Hemenway, as she then was. But from the very first it was overwhelmingly clear that this was something wholly different. We started to "go together," as one then said, in my junior year. There never was any question in my mind about the future. When Mary graduated and I was staying on for my fifth year, and although we had no admitted understanding about the future, I gave her a set of the eleventh edition of the *Encyclopaedia Britannica* as a graduating present. She was going to teach school—Latin and History—in a very small town in New Mexico and she needed resources. But that wasn't my idea at all. Clearly the Weaver household of the future ought to have a good edition of the *Britannica,* and this was a suitable time to acquire it.

Those who know us do not need any written statement to the effect that Mary is at the same time my best friend and my own true love. Others would not be interested, but I have written this down and I will let it stand. Along with all the rest, I am as proud of her as I am of my son and daughter, and I can make no stronger affirmation than that.

3. Throop/Caltech

In the late spring of 1917 Dr. Robert A. Millikan (1868–1953)—the Nobel Prize measurer of the electrical charge of the electron—asked me to come to see him in Chicago. This was just at the time when Dr. Millikan was shifting his interests to Pasadena, spending one academic quarter there each year, at the institution then known as Throop College but soon to be renamed the California Institute of Technology.

I had never seen Dr. Millikan previous to this interview; but he was a good friend of Mason's and had heard of me from that source. I was at once charmed by this handsome, friendly, great man. He said, "I understand you have been studying electrodynamics under Dr. Max Mason."

"That's correct," I replied.

"Do you understand it?" he asked.

That was a poser. The interview might terminate abruptly if I said no, and it would be pretentious or even arrogant to say yes. So I said, "Dr. Millikan, I wonder if you would be willing to make the question somewhat more specific."

From his desk he picked up the classic German text *Lehrbuch der Elektrodynamik* by Max Abraham (1875–1922) and August Otto Föppl (1854–1924), asked me if I had read it, opened it at random, pointed to the double page, and said, "Tell me what this is about."

Fortunately I knew that volume backwards and forwards, and the passage involved was one with which I was very familiar; so at once I sketched for him the discussion of those and a few following pages. He said at once, "All right. Very good. Would you like to go out to Throop College with me next fall?" I agreed without delay, and September 1917 saw me in Pasadena.

Soon after arriving, both elated and nervous that I was to teach calculus for the first time, I went to the college bookstore—actually only a counter on the ground floor of Throop Hall—and asked what text was to be used in the course. The girl smiled and said, "Why don't you wait until tomorrow, when your teacher will tell you?" The gap between the 125-pound assistant professor and the husky Western freshmen was small indeed.

In those days the physical plant of the college consisted of Throop Hall, a chemistry building, and, in the orchard back of Throop Hall, the so-called Old Dorm and the "Greasy Spoon" (which had been moved there from the previous location in North Las Robles). The faculty was so small that its meetings were held in the modest-sized office of President James A. B. Scherer. But on the walls of the President's office were the drawings of the distinguished architect Bertram C. Goodhue, portraying a dream for a great future—a dream which was viewed by some at that time with great skepticism, but a dream that was destined to come to pass.

I thoroughly enjoyed my work. I was proud and happy to be accepted as a colleague by the rest of the faculty. Although the institution is now recognized as one of the top leaders in our country, it was then modest in its equipment and largely local in its reputation, but nevertheless it already had some very able men on its faculty and—even more important—it was turbulent with fresh ideas and high ideals. A small engineering school with only the early beginnings of a real science faculty, it was dedicated to the proposition that engineers be solidly grounded in basic science and that scientists be thoroughly trained in the humanities.

The first year at Throop was not lacking in highlights for me. We had a rather sharp earthquake, which hit when I was sitting in my desk chair, tipped back against its spring suspension, so that I got a specially big initial shake. This event cleared up, as far as I am concerned, the often debated question as to whether one hears an earthquake in advance. I certainly did hear a strange, low-frequency sound. We had, for further excitement, a fire on nearby Mount Wilson. There always was, with fires in that locality, the special risk that the great observatory might be harmed; so the students (and the younger teachers) all were released from classes and transported up to fight the fire.

There was also a lively tradition that the students go on a rampage from time to time. This tradition has been maintained; not many years ago Cal Tech students stealthily but ingeniously got possession of the code for the display of the colored cards in the rooters' section for a football game in the Rose Bowl. They replaced the code by a modified one so that the amazed spectators saw, in the colored card display, references to Cal Tech instead of the teams actually playing.

One of the civil engineering professors was wont to bore his classes with the account of a bridge he had designed; so one spring evening the boys got into his office, used several desks, tables, and chairs to build a ceiling-high "bridge" naughtily labeled in his honor; and then when leaving poured all the door locks full of hot glue. It may have been on that same evening that the boys painted the nude statue of Apollo which occupied the most conspicuous position opposite the entrance of Throop Hall, using lavender, scarlet, and green for his, shall I say, less public features.

Some academic institutions spring fully developed not from the forehead of Jove but from the hip pocket of an inspired multimillionaire, but the California Institute of Technology had a curiously interesting origin. In 1891, Amos Gager Throop, a wealthy retired Chicago businessman, alderman, and enthusiastic Universalist, decided to found an academic institution at Pasadena. He overambitiously named it Throop University, and it was indeed his original idea that in addition to a school of letters and science, it should have a law school, a musical institute, an art studio, and faculties devoted to elocution, stenography and typewriting, and physical culture. He may have had grandiose ideas, but he also had a grand idea, for "he was determined that it should be the best." [1] *

The "University" opened on November 2, 1891, but by the following March it had become evident that too much had been attempted, and the trustees decided to concentrate on "a Manual Training Institution . . . second to none in the land," and to change the name to Throop

*Numbers in the text refer to Reference Notes in the back of the book.

Polytechnic Institute. This coeducational institution started with thirty students, but it prospered and grew.

Besides the college and the normal branches, it developed a preparatory school called the academy, and a subpreparatory school renamed the grammar school. By 1905 it had begun to shift emphasis from the junior work and the manual training to engineering, and by 1907 there were 529 students enrolled.

In the fall of 1906 a critical event occurred there. Norman Bridges, the chairman of the Board of Trustees of Throop Polytechnic, called on George Ellery Hale (1868–1938), the great American astronomer who had founded the Mount Wilson observatory, and asked, "What can we do to become first class?" Hale's reply was, "Scrap practically the whole thing and start over." In April 1907, the trustees voted to make the institution "a high-grade technical school," decided to abandon the elementary school, and appointed James A. B. Scherer the new president. It was Hale who found the new president, as it was Hale who, from this point on, was a chief guiding spirit.

In this reorganization there were retained only a college and an academy, but the latter was doomed by the fact that many good polytechnical high schools were then being developed in Southern California. The academy was discontinued and Throop Institute, now exclusively a college, opened on its new and present campus in the fall of 1910. That year there was a total of thirty-one students, but the determination to maintain quality was demonstrated by the fact that only fifteen freshmen were admitted, although thirty-three applied.

In 1913 Throop Polytechnic Institute became Throop College of Technology. That same year Hale brought to the college Arthur Amos Noyes (1866–1936), the distinguished American chemist who had been vice-president (and for a time acting president) of Massachusetts Institute of Technology. Noyes originally agreed to spend February and March at Pasadena, but by 1916 he was there at least half of each year. During 1916–1917 Hale brought Robert A. Millikan there for the first time, again originally for three months of the year.

In 1919 Noyes resigned at MIT to give full time to Throop. After World War I, Millikan resumed his annual three months at Pasadena as director of physical research. When Scherer's health failed, the trustees used every effort to have Millikan replace him, and he was in fact offered the presidency in April 1921. Dr. Millikan accepted the offer with the condition that he not be named president, but be designated chairman of the Executive Council, which consisted of three trustees and three faculty members. The institution he led was the California Institute of Technology, for the trustees of Throop College of Technology voted that change in name at their final meeting in February 1920. The timing of the transition was just such as to permit me to be an assistant professor of Throop and then an assistant professor of Caltech.

Although many doubtless think of Caltech as the MIT of the West Coast, it may not be widely recognized that there was an original close connection, not large in numbers but large indeed in spirit and significance, between MIT and CIT. For not only was the MIT professor and vice-president, Noyes, one of the three great human forces in the development of CIT, Dr. Hale, at the western end of the bridge, was sufficiently valued by MIT so that he was offered the presidency of the eastern institute in 1906.

The role of these three men, Hale, Noyes, and Millikan, in creating Caltech was so important that it is hard to evaluate. Certainly it cannot be overestimated. Everyone who was there at that time had the greatest respect and admiration for all three. They were, first and foremost, great scholars and splendid persons. Although all were great practical assets from the point of view of public relations and, to be blunt about it, money raising, Rob Millikan was the supreme artist at this. He could talk to an audience of fifty middle-aged or elderly wealthy women and come away with fifty permanent and fanatically devoted allies.

The most complex of the three was unquestionably Millikan. He was completely dedicated to his students, and would, without any public knowledge, lend them his personal funds; but he rigorously insisted that his name go down as senior author on scientific papers, even including some for which he had written not a word. Though he had refused the title of president, as chairman of the Executive Council he ruled with all the devious dexterity of a dictator, making private oral commitments that would have been fatal had it not been for his power to meet any emergency with a smiling new triumph.

I suppose that once in a great while a colt is foaled on the blue grass meadows of Kentucky that so obviously has all the attributes of future greatness as to be evident from the first. Certainly it was perfectly clear, when I went there just a half century ago, that Caltech was destined for greatness. In addition to the great triumvirate, there were outstandingly fine and able men on the faculty—Royal W. Sorenson, a great electrical engineer; Franklin Thomas, a distinguished civil engineer; Stuart J. Bates in physical chemistry; Harry Bateman in mathematics; Clinton K. Judy in literature.

One day at a faculty meeting President Scherer unrolled an impressive scroll, sat looking at it, and explained to us that it was an invitation from a large sister institution to send a representative to the celebration of their fiftieth anniversary. He handed the scroll to Professor Judy with the remark, "Perhaps you will read this to the group here."

Professor Judy looked thoughtfully at the scroll, and then began, in his rich, deep voice, to read to us the elegantly phrased and dignified sentences of the invitation. After he returned it, showing no surprise or any other emotion, Dr. Scherer said, "Well, gentlemen, I guess I must explain that the joke is on me: the document is written in Latin."

I doubt whether many small engineering colleges had a professor of literature who could have equaled that performance. But then I doubt whether many small engineering colleges of that time had student assemblies at which Amelita Galli-Curci sang, or the Los Angeles Symphony Orchestra played, or John Masefield spoke. Not many such schools were then (or now) demanding that the engineering students take a course in the English department *every semester of their four years*. Not many small technological institutions had such a poet as Alfred Noyes as a Lecturer in English Literature—as we did in 1920–1921.

During my first year there were just four graduate students. In mathematics—how unbelievable in retrospect —the most advanced courses for the engineers were a first course in differential equations, a course in advanced calculus, and a course in least squares which I taught! But by

1919–1920, when I went back after World War I, there were nine graduate students and the growth had begun.

There was considerable scientific activity at Throop, which, in the early months of our national participation in World War I was oriented toward defense, particularly in the aeronautical area. The submarine menace being an obvious and indeed a terrifying one, there also were various studies related to high-frequency sound production, transmission, and detection. I read up on the piezoelectric effect, whereby a block of crystal can be electrically driven to oscillate at high frequencies. Harry Bateman, the English mathematician previously mentioned, was investigating, with his powerful but extremely theoretical methods, the possible advantage of electrically driving a hollow spherical shell of crystal, so that it could be used as a source of underwater sound waves. One day I asked him how serious would be the effect of the discontinuity where the two halves of the hollow spherical shell were cemented to form a complete hollow sphere. It turned out that Harry had not thought of that. He just calmly assumed that some practical chap could put a concentric spherical hole inside a solid crystal sphere without tampering in any way with its homogeneity! Bateman had been a First Wrangler at Trinity College, Cambridge, was a profound scholar with a vast store of knowledge about partial differential equations, and a sweet and gentle person. But he was not precisely practical.

Toward the end of the spring semester at Throop in 1918 I was inducted into service at the request of Charles E. Mendenhall, Chairman of the Physics Department at the University of Wisconsin. Mendenhall was then a major in an organization closely related to the National Research Council, set up in World War I (as was Vannevar Bush's Office of Scientific Research and Development in World War II) to bring science to the service of the armed forces. I went in as a private, but after some months was made a second lieutenant.

I worked chiefly at the Bureau of Standards in Washington, in a group which—how ridiculous and ineffective this seems in retrospect—consisted of myself and an expert mechanic. There were few aircraft flight instruments available in those days, and I was primarily concerned with the design and test of turn and bank indicators. It was very easy to design and construct a gyroscopic device that would tell the pilots when they were flying in a straight line. But bank indicators, especially ones which would continue to operate with useful accuracy during the acrobatics of aerial dogfights, presented difficulties we never overcame. I did get to do some very exciting acrobatic flying at Langley Field, where returned fighter pilots would subject the instruments (and the testing scientist!) to the latest flying tricks. But this was not the sort of participation in the war I craved, and I was relieved when I was discharged.

I did not return directly to Pasadena, but finished out the spring semester of 1919 at Wisconsin, where the shortage of teachers was so acute that they were glad to give me temporary employment.

Late in the summer of 1919 I went down to Carlsbad, New Mexico, where Mary was living. We were married there on September 1, this date being after my twenty-fifth birthday but three days before Mary's twenty-fifth. According to her discontinuous theory of ages she was twenty-four until the day when she became twenty-five, so she had the satisfaction of being "one year younger" than I on our marriage day. In the evening of our wedding day we were driven in a broken-down Ford by a local New Mexico character to the nearby town of Artesia, so that we could there catch the train for Los Angeles. The lights on the car became very dim, and our driver contributed a permanent saying to our family vocabulary by remarking that "The Ford's got the sorriest lights in the world." He also commented wryly on what he called "the stubble" of the cottonwood trees, giving that word an extended meaning which has also become part of our private patois.

The trip west on the Sante Fe Chief was our only honeymoon excursion. I think Mary has never really forgiven me for not stopping to see the Grand Canyon—it was a good deal like a newly married couple passing through Niagara without stopping to see the Falls. I made this up to her later.

At Pasadena we lived in a room for a few days and then rented a small but adequate cottage at 789 South Mentor, about a ten-minute walk from my office at the college. It was modest indeed, but it had two palms, an orange tree, two very prolific lemon trees, and a loquat tree. It fit our $1,800 salary very well, for the rent was $17 a month. Our first guests for a meal were Ethel and Harry Bateman.

We had been married less than a month before I was horrified to learn that my wife knew absolutely no physics. With naïve and, as it turned out, entirely misguided zeal, I decided I must teach her. I brought home the first volume of the introductory text by Robert Millikan and Henry Gale, and we started to read it aloud.

All our long life together we have read aloud, and with

the greatest mutual pleasure. As I write these lines my wife is waiting for me to stop and read to her while she knits—in this particular instance the book being Lawrance Thompson's fine biography of Robert Frost. But a physics text turned out to be a very poor start for the reading program. Things went not too badly for a few pages, but then we came to the first equation, $f = ma$, or force equals mass times acceleration. Mary promptly fell off the toboggan, and has been off ever since.

I was in love, and I didn't propose that force, mass, or acceleration should come between us; but this was a disturbing experience. It was, in fact, the beginning of my education to the fact that there are various complementary ways of approaching life and its problems, the logical and usually quantitative procedures of science constituting one good way, and the intuitive, artistic, and more philosophical approach being an equally valid way.

This first year of married life was as idyllic as the storybooks say it ought to be. My work was engrossing. We both hugely enjoyed the privilege of attending the luxurious Presbyterian church on Colorado Street, where we heard truly wonderful sermons by Robert Freeman. We hiked up into the mountains, sometimes acting as overnight chaperones for two student couples we liked very much. Ernest Watson, later to be Dean of the College but at that time a very special sort of assistant to Millikan, took us on an occasional trip in Dr. Millikan's car, of which he had the use. We had the earth by the tail with a downhill pull.

In the spring of 1920 I received communications from Dean Slichter and from Max Mason, as well as the more official word from George Clark Sellery, the Dean of the College of Letters and Science at the University of Wisconsin. They wanted me to come back. Max said, "We can work together—in fact, let's write a book on electromagnetic field theory." This was irresistible.

In response to my note to him Dr. Millikan sent me a handwritten letter:

> Dear Warren:
>
> If you insist on going back to the University of Wisconsin, of course I can't stop you. But I can refuse to accept your resignation. In fact I do not accept your resignation, and you will continue to be a professor of The California Institute of Technology, on leave until your return.
>
> Very cordially yours,
> Robert A. Millikan

I have had the pleasure, several times over the years, of reminding the authorities of Caltech that they live under the threat of my return.

4. Teaching at Wisconsin

In September 1920, we returned to Madison and lived there for nearly twelve years. I went back to the university as an assistant professor, was made an associate professor in 1925, and a professor and chairman of the department in 1928. The previous chairman had been Edward Burr Van Vleck, a distinguished mathematician, a discriminating collector of Japanese art, and a gentle scholar of the old school. He asked to be relieved, over his last year of teaching, of the administrative duties of the chairmanship —duties which he carried out with characteristically conscientious, meticulous care, but duties which he clearly did not relish. When the chairmanship was offered to me I went to Professor Van Vleck, for whom I had a great respect, admiration, and affection, and asked him if I could count on his help, for I was only thirty-four, whereas the other full professors were all considerably older and more experienced.

At that point I learned a lesson I have never forgotten. Van Vleck gently but firmly told me that when a person retired from a position he should do so completely, leaving his successor entirely free. Following this policy, he would never volunteer any suggestion, nor would he ever express any criticism. Indeed he made it clear that he would prefer that I not ask his advice even on some explicit point, for he thought that he should take his hand completely off and leave the problems to me. The courtesy, friendliness, and confidence with which he handled this situation were a great inspiration to me. Ever since, whenever I left an assignment of any sort, I remembered that lesson. I have never had any interest in influencing the choice of the person to follow me, nor in extending the policies I have favored. I have great confidence in younger people, and in the future. I believe, as someone has said, that "nothing succeeds like a successor," especially if you give him a chance. This episode also made me realize the importance of retiring from any activity at a moment when one's departure is the occasion for regret, not relief.

I was so fond of teaching that I got up each morning with zestful enthusiasm for the day's tasks. My teaching was initially to engineers—one or at most two classes of elementary analysis and of calculus, and one junior or senior course. After a few years I also taught a graduate course in the physics department, so that my engineering courses were reduced to one for underclassmen and one for juniors or seniors. About every other summer I had the privilege— we thought of it as such—of teaching in the six-week or even in the nine-week summer session. The former paid, at the start, $250; and this was by no means a negligible addition to income. Also one got a chance to offer short new courses in topics of current interest.

If there is a better life than that of an enthusiastic teacher in a good school, I don't know what it is! The income was so very modest that a raise in salary of $500 was an exciting satisfaction. One's friends were on similar salaries; one could live decently, could pay his bills, and could even make a monthly deposit in the babies' educational savings account. The family could have a resident student helping with meals and washing dishes for room and board. There was little keeping up with the Joneses, for Dr. Jones was also an assistant professor.

The life was rich and rewarding in so many ways. About half of my lunches were at home, to be followed by a completely quiet afternoon in my study. About half were with stimulating colleagues at the University Club. There was good talk at table, where one's companions might be philosophers, or historians, or physicians, specialists in medieval literature, or whatever. There was a gay and spirited game of billiards after lunch, before going back to the office.

This, moreover, was back in those good old days when professors had summer vacations—nearly three months every other summer, and half that, other times. One could renew his spirit, and when the first smoky tang of autumn came into the air, there was an almost compulsive yearning to get back on the campus and see the throngs of excited (and exciting) new youngsters, to regather with colleagues, to be back in the classroom meeting the challenge of a new group of eager minds. The registration in that new advanced subject—would it be only three or four—which would worry the dean? Or would it be six or eight—which would be splendid. Or would it be twelve or fifteen—which would be phenomenal! The intoxication of a September day on the campus is a reward that can hardly be understood by those who are condemned to earning their living in more prosaic ways.

We had church friends, neighborhood friends, and family friends, and we also had the automatically assured group of faculty friends—men and women of wide experience, varied interests, great competence. There were faculty wives' groups, and occasions—such as the Madison Literary

Club—which husbands and wives both attended. But the men had a special privilege—their dining clubs. These met once a month or oftener, and in the tradition of the great English clubs of the seventeenth century, had a splendid meal followed by a long evening of serious discussion. I belonged to three such clubs. The one with the youngest membership was a group of what the medical fraternity would call the "young Turks," being of less conventional, not to say radical, temperament. My keenest memory of this group is of a long and noisy evening in my own home, during which Philip Fox La Follette (later the Governor of Wisconsin) and I hotly debated the practical effectiveness and moral justification of capital punishment, I being in favor and he opposed. A second dining club was a research group, and at each meeting the host had the responsibility of giving a generally intelligible account of his own scholarly activities. The third, to which I was not elected until I had been back in Madison for several years, was a distinguished organization that had been in existence for a long time. It was called Town & Gown, and as its name implies, it included, among its normal quota of twelve, equal representation from the university and from the City of Madison. Town & Gown has met regularly since 1878. Its roster includes several of the university's most eminent presidents, including Charles Richard Van Hise and Edward Asahel Birge; scholars such as Frederick J. Turner, Moses Stephen Slaughter, Joseph Jastrow, and John R. Commons; judges, justices of the supreme court, and governors.

My father died in the autumn of 1921—he was killed in a hunting accident. Afterwards we were even closer than previously to my stepmother, Cicely. We spent the entire day together, each Sunday after church. Late in the afternoon we would start reading aloud. I especially recall the pleasure with which we meandered through Anthony Trollope's Barchester Chronicles. My very modest inheritance furnished the down payment on a new house, which an architect friend of ours designed.

Our son, Warren Weaver, Jr., was born in 1923. Always devoted to working with my hands, as each Christmas approached I laid plans for making some major present for our small son. One year it was a large chest of blocks, all carefully made from clear sugar pine. One year it was a case with a huge collection of lead soldiers, mounted and unmounted. Evenings after he was tucked in, I cast them in molds, trimmed and painted them, and made the case, in the basement. Our daughter Helen was not born until near the end of our Madison period, in 1931. Our family life during all this period was as happy as I can conceive of family life being.

I took off one semester and did research related to electrical and magnetic methods of ore location for the firm of Mason, Slichter, and Hay. Max, Louis Slichter, and Don Hay had been associated in brilliantly successful work on submarine detection problems during World War I, and after the war they had important, and at that time novel, ideas for new techniques of geophysical prospecting. One summer, in 1928, I taught electrodynamics at the University of Chicago.

I had a number of especially gifted American students who went on to distinguished careers—Lee A. Du Bridge as President of California Institute of Technology (now adviser to President Nixon), Leland J. Haworth as Director of the National Science Foundation, and John Bardeen, winner of the Nobel Prize for physics in 1956, to name only three. One engineering undergraduate, since become famous, I chanced not to have in any of my classes. He departed from the university somewhat precipitously, leaving in the mathematics department a record of "Incomplete" in calculus. On May 22, 1927, I got his card out of the department file, and in view of the event of the preceding day, wrote "Incomplete removed" on the record of Charles A. Lindbergh.

The primary incentive in coming back to Madison was to work with Max Mason, and our collaboration promptly commenced. We were well suited to work together, for we complemented each other in several ways. Max really didn't like to work, and I did; in particular he despised writing whereas I enjoyed it. He did not relish a disciplined schedule, and it was congenial to me to set up and maintain one. He had, of course, at least 90 per cent of the brains of the combination and probably 99 per cent of the imagination; but no matter how severe his criticism of a passage, I was always willing to go back at it for another try. We worked together almost every day for a couple of hours, and I would customarily put in at least that many hours by myself. At that time there was no exposition of electromagnetic field theory that made full use of the nimble power of vector calculus, or that attempted to carry out the transition from the unitary laws for isolated electric charge to the continuous laws for the large-scale field occupying all of space. We made very rough going of certain aspects of this latter point, for it was of course the case that there was no solid-state theory available at that time.

As our book neared completion I became more and more discouraged about it; for it grew increasingly clear that Max was never going to be really satisfied with it. In 1925, moreover, Max was chosen to be president of the University of Chicago, so that I was working mostly alone, writing to him often and sending him drafts, but getting little response. Finally he realized that this was unreasonable and authorized me to submit the manuscript. *The Electromagnetic Field* was published in 1929. It got good reviews, and for some twenty years thereafter, a fair proportion of graduate students in physics learned Maxwell's field equations, and all the associated theory, from our book. I was specially pleased that the volume was chosen by the American Institute of Graphic Arts as one of the Fifty Books of the Year of 1929, this referring not at all to its contents but to its typography, binding, and general design. I am still occasionally introduced to a physicist who blinks and says, "Weaver, of Mason and Weaver?"

The twenties were very heady times in physics. Both relativity and quantum theory were being vigorously pursued. The physics department at Madison had a series of stimulating visitors. The first of these, and one of the great masters of the older school, was H. A. Lorentz, who was present for a special colloquium in 1922.* Arnold J. W. Sommerfeld (1868–1951), the world-famous physicist from Göttingen, was there for an extended visit in 1923, following which we had visits from a succession of such leaders

*There seem to be no available departmental or other university records of these visitors, and the dates stated may be slightly in error.

as the German theoretical physicists and specialists in wave mechanics Erwin Schrödinger (1887–1961), Werner Heisenberg, Gregor Wentzel, and the British physicist Paul Adrien Maurice Dirac, and the British mathematician and astrophysicist Sir Ralph Howard Fowler. Particularly from Schrödinger, Dirac, and Heisenberg we had a chance to hear about quantum theory and wave mechanics from the geniuses who were just then creating these fields.

If it had not been for Max's attitude, I think I would doubtless have plunged overboard into these subjects. But he was sarcastically indifferent. I think he must have admired the formal analytical skill of these outstanding men, but he was convinced that all this was futilely and falsely oriented. His objections bore no relation to the claim of Albert Einstein (1879–1955) in his famous debate with the Danish physicist Niels Bohr (1885–1962)—that there must be an underlying deterministic and discoverable reality in nature and that the basic laws of nature were not subject to chance. I am sure that Max had no intellectual or artistic objection to an inherently probabilistic theory; what he could not tolerate were the inconsistencies between these newer theories and the older classical field theories, the internal inconsistencies in quantum theory, and what he viewed to be the artificially introduced and essentially unpleasant "messiness" of the newer theories.

The steadily increasing record of success of the theories did not particularly impress him. Indeed it must be conceded that capacity to deal with more and more experiential fact is not, of itself, a hallmark of a beautiful theory. One could, to be absurd, print all the known facts in a huge volume and inscribe on the first page, "This entire volume constitutes the theory." This would obviously be wholly unsatisfactory, and makes clear that a good theory, in addition to dealing with a wide range of facts, should exhibit a sort of poetic concentration and simplicity, the wide scope opening up from a small central unified core. A really good theory, in short, has to have what mathematicians usually call "elegance." As Henri Poincaré showed long ago, moreover, if there is one theory which successfully deals with a body of experience, then there are indefinitely many theories which accomplish the same task. So again, mere "success" is not enough to lead to the choice of a theory.

Under heavy influence from Max, and being at the same time too busy with the combination of family, teaching, and electrodynamics to take the necessary time to become really versed in quantum theory, I adopted his attitude; and I must say that I have never changed it. I still think that quantum mechanics, despite its magnificent and detailed triumphs, is a disposable portion of science which we will some day discard *in toto*, to replace it by something which will be even more competent and which will be much more satisfying, something whose complications are but the external aspects of an inner simplicity—something, in short, more elegant.

My dislike of quantum theory in the twenties, when it was in process of vigorous elaboration, was due in major part to the fact that it was not compatible with classical electromagnetic theory—the latter field being one that I was both very familiar with and very fond of.

As the years have gone by I have developed a more seriously based antagonism to quantum theory. Toward the end of this book I will indicate the basis for this more serious objection.

5. The Rockefeller Foundation

During my teaching years at Madison, the University of Wisconsin, although modest in size by today's standards, was the dominant factor in the life of the capital city. The atmosphere of the university was one of calm dedication to the pursuit of knowledge. Student disturbances never occurred on any significant scale; the relationships of students, faculty, and administration were characterized by friendly respect.

Madison was an attractive city of modest size, so that the university set the tone of the whole community. To be a teacher there was most pleasant in every way. And yet it was, as I soon came to realize, a somewhat isolated and circumscribed life, with a built-in tendency to provincialism. Only the rare professor who had sufficient private resources could indulge in European or wider travel. Great art, great music, great theater were all rather inaccessible. We tended to develop insulated interests and concerns, and to be rather naïvely satisfied with our lot and all our surroundings.

My own personal doors and windows to the wider world had been opened a small crack when the family moved from a tiny rural village to the state capital. But these doors and windows were to be flung wide in 1932 by another and far more drastic change of scene.

For in the late fall of 1931 I had had a phone call from New York City. It was Max Mason. Would I come to New York to discuss the possibility of joining the staff of the Rockefeller Foundation?

This was not only wholly unexpected—it was very upsetting. Things were going very well at the university, and there were even rumors of a significant promotion. We had that special set of close friends which is characteristic of a couple's first married years. Our young son was happy in a good school. We loved our new house, and in particular I was so pleased with a study just then built into our third floor that I was quite content to believe that here I was as near heaven as I would ever ascend. Furthermore, we both had our roots in the Middle West, and neither of us had any interest in big cities—we knew Chicago, but as a place we disliked, and to which one went only on the occasion of a mathematics convention, or when one needed to shop at Marshall Field's or wanted to go to the theater. Why should we leave Madison for anywhere?

A request from Max, however, was not to be disregarded, nor was there sense in turning down a free trip to New York City, which I had never seen.

Arriving at the Rockefeller Foundation offices and being asked my ideas about their program in supporting science, I explained that, satisfied as I was with being immersed in the physical sciences, I was convinced that the great wave of the future in science, a wave not yet gathering its strength, was to occur in the biological sciences. The startling visions that were just then beginning to open up in genetics, in cellular physiology, in biochemistry, in developmental mechanics—these were due for tremendously significant advances.

It seemed clear to me that the Rockefeller Foundation had a great opportunity. Although they had been very active and very successful in public health and medicine, their program in the "Natural Sciences" (the term they used for everything in science other than medicine) had put major emphasis on the physical sciences, including large support for astronomy. This had been more than justified, and had paid great dividends. Indeed these dividends are still coming in, as for example from the large 1928 grant to construct the 200-inch telescope on Mount Palomar. But despite my personal commitment to the physical sciences, I strongly felt that the Rockefeller Foundation ought to undertake a large and long-range support of quantitative biology.

This was by no means a uniquely inspired conviction, for others had the same idea, notably the German physiologist and Nobel Laureate Otto Warburg, who had written:

". . . the most important problem in biology is to obtain an understanding in physiochemical terms of the processes—and the substances which take part in these processes—that occur in the normal living cell." [1]

The idea that the time was ripe for a great new change in biology was substantiated by the fact that the physical sciences had by then elaborated a whole battery of analytical and experimental procedures capable of probing into nature with a fineness and with a quantitative precision that would tremendously supplement the previous tools of biology—one can almost say "the previous tool" of biology, since the optical microscope had furnished so large a proportion of the detailed evidence.

Even at that time, more than thirty-five years ago, one could identify some of the procedures and the instruments that were ready to be applied more intensively to basic biological problems. Although a practical working instrument had not yet been built, it was known that a microscope using ultraviolet light could discriminate detail about ten times as fine as that analyzable by a microscope using ordinary light. Indeed the wave aspects of quantum theory indicated that an electron microscope—although the working models were then some few years off—could reveal details at least a thousand times finer. More indirect ways of analyzing structure—extensions of the ordinary processes of seeing—were soon to be available through the use of X ray and electron diffraction studies.

In addition to new ways to see in greater and more revealing detail, there was a rich promise of new ways to separate out the constituents of complicated biological systems such as blood and the other fluids of the body. The supercentrifuge of the Swedish chemist Theodor Svedberg, for example, was already available.

When one today looks through the massive annual issue of *Science* which is devoted to equipment, he realizes the tremendous range and power of the instrumentation— much of it employing automatic electronic techniques— now available for quantitative experimentation in biology and medicine. This was of course not foreseeable in any detailed way during 1931–1932. But enough was discernible to convince one that biology was about to have the tools to enable it to enter upon a new era.

Although I was convinced that the Rockefeller Foundation ought to move in this direction, it seemed even clearer to me that I was not qualified to direct such a program. I told this emphatically to the top officers of the foundation. But as I was enthusiastically convinced of the importance of moving in that direction, and because I did have the necessary background in the physical sciences, they somewhat rashly, as it seemed to me, offered me the directorship of that division of the Rockefeller Foundation dealing with all aspects of science other than professionally medical.

I took the train to Madison in a confused state of mind, excited but disturbed.

Back home, my wife and I cast up the account of pros and cons. There seemed to be so many reasons for continuing the contented and assured life we had in Madison. We recognized some real disadvantages in going to New York: we were convinced we would never really like living there; and we assumed that we would never have friends comparable to the first young group. The salary was substantially larger, but that actually did not seem important to us. We realized that there was a sort of Parkinson's Law for the personal budget, assuring that extra salary would promptly be absorbed in extra expenses.

There was, of course, the promise of wide travel, that being an attraction, but also a burden to a family that loved its life together. We debated the issue day after day. Finally I said, "After all, we must make up our minds," and my wife replied, "Of course we *have* made up our minds." And of course we had, not because of desire, but because we realized that this was a greater opportunity than would ever again face us. We could not go on living with ourselves unless we met the challenge.

I think, also, that I was both realistic and accurate about my abilities and my limitations. I loved to teach, and knew that I had been successful at it. I had a good capacity for assimilating information, something of a knack for organizing, an ability to work with people, a zest for exposition, an enthusiasm that helped to advance my ideas. But I lacked that strange and wonderful creative spark that makes a good researcher.

Thus I realized that there was a definite ceiling on my possibilities as a mathematics professor. Indeed, I think I realized that I was already about as far up in that profession as I was likely to go. So this offer opened whole new possibilities for me. We began to pack.

The first days in the great city and with the wholly strange new job were confusing indeed. My wife, in fact, was literally and unpleasantly dizzy most of the time during the first few months.

We were temporarily settled in an apartment on upper Fifth Avenue. The trip down to the office, then at 61 Broadway, had to be made by subway. I got detailed instructions about which train to take and where to change, but on my very first ride, after what I feared was too long a journey between stations, I felt pressure in my ears, and realized I must be in a tunnel under the East River, heading by mistake for the wilds of Brooklyn. I got out at the next stop, emerged to the surface, found myself in utterly strange surroundings, and in complete bewilderment got into a cab and said "61 Broadway." I was late to work on the first morning.

The sweep of the new job was at once apparent. My first interview related to the Highlands Museum in North Carolina, the second to geophysics at Harvard, and the third to the undergraduate science curriculum of the University of Yencheng in China, an institution that was training young Chinese who wished to get subsequent medical training at the Peking Union Medical College, which had been developed under Rockefeller Foundation support. I had been in the office less than three months—barely long enough to learn the mechanics of the procedures—when I left for Europe, taking the family along. The insular Midwesterner had to have his horizons opened up.

This was the first trip abroad for us, and there was so much to learn. I had fair German, but only rudimentary oral French, so that language was at once a problem. We established ourselves in a pension at St. Cloud, a short commuting train ride outside Paris, where was located the European office of the Rockefeller Foundation. Even getting to the office presented a language difficulty. It was on a street only one block long—Rue de la Baume. Unless you pronounced the address to suit the extremely critical and never very accommodating judgment of the Paris taxi drivers, you found yourself being rushed to the Rue de la Pompe, way out in the 16th Arrondissement. The safeguard was to say, firmly, "Rue de la Baume, *entre Percier et Courcelles,*" the latter being the two better-known adjoining streets.

We arrived in Paris late in April, when that marvelous city was lovely indeed.

At that time the principal office of the Rockefeller Foundation, other than the home office in New York, was the one in Paris. The Division of Natural Sciences, of which I was the young and inexperienced chief, had three officers more or less permanently based in Paris. Two of these were primarily concerned with fellowship activities. It was their job to travel to universities and research centers and seek out the most promising young scientists, to offer them the chance to spend a year or even two wherever in the world they could have the best opportunity to broaden and improve their training. In those days fellowship opportunities of that sort were rare indeed, and the Rockefeller Foundation appointments were highly prized and eagerly sought.

The other and more senior science officer based in Paris was Professor Lauder W. Jones, an organic chemist on leave from Princeton. The three science officers shared the responsibility of studying all requests for aid that originated in Europe, and of forwarding their recommendations to the main office in New York.

Lauder Jones was comfortable in both French and German. He hugely enjoyed travel, partly for the obvious reasons, and partly because he was a gourmet who loved to sample the best food and wines of every region of Europe. He had a fabulous memory, and when he and I went to a new city—new to me, that is—he always gave me a long lecture on its most distinguished cafés and restaurants, its food specialties, and the noteworthy local wines. He was acquainted with every maître d'hôtel, and more particularly with every cellarman, wherever we went. On my first trips with him I absorbed a great deal of knowledge about European universities, institutes, and scientific leaders, and I absorbed a great deal more besides.

During the first few months when I was based in the Paris office, I traveled with Lauder Jones to essentially all of the university centers of western and southwestern Europe, and we made particularly extensive visits in Scandinavia and in England. At the larger centers we would spend several days, meeting the local scientific leaders, learning about their facilities and the problems that chiefly concerned them, being especially interested to discover any deficiencies in equipment, personnel assistance, or support that might be preventing these leaders from realizing their full potential. We were insistent about meeting the promising younger persons, passing back to our colleagues in Paris any suggestions about attractive fellowship candidates.

At the larger institutions we made systematic departmental visits, aimed at getting an understanding of that institution's primary interests in physics, biology, chemistry, and other sciences, the character and quality of leadership, and the nature of the institution's most important resources. Going to a smaller and more remote place, we would characteristically be seeking contact with some one outstanding man, the excellence of whose work had attracted general attention. And we did indeed go to a considerable number of less famous universities—for example in the Baltic states, in Finland, and in southeastern Europe.

These first tours were almost wholly different from the later visits. The Rockefeller Foundation had a high reputation in Europe, owing largely to the qualifications of the officers who had, previous to my time, dealt with the institutions there, and also, of course, owing to the considerable financial support with which the Rockefeller Foundation had aided European scholarship. Therefore, this being the initial set of visits of a new head of a major division of the foundation, there inevitably was a considerable amount of ceremony and of official attention. We met with all of the great scientific figures of Europe and were formally entertained by many of them. To give a little of the flavor of those first days in European university centers, let me recount the program for just one day, not untypical of this first tour, but very untypical of later visits.

On May 12, 1932, Lauder Jones and I left Paris on

the night train for Munich. Arriving there the next morning, we established ourselves at the splendid hotel, the Vier Jahreszeiten, and we were presently called on by Professor Karl von Frisch, the Austrian-German zoologist who has since become very famous for his studies of the ways in which bees communicate. Professor von Frisch took us to visit the old Institute of Zoology, located in a monastery. The Rockefeller Foundation had made grants to enable them to build a new Institute of Zoology at Munich, as well as a new Institute of Physical Chemistry. Near a well in the courtyard he showed us some of his current experiments with bees.

At one o'clock we went to the Rathaus (the town hall) where we were officially entertained by the Oberbürgermeister (the mayor) and the other principal city officials, along with the Göttingen physicist Arnold Sommerfeld (an old friend of mine), Von Frisch, the physical chemist Kasimir Fajans, then professor of chemistry at Munich, and others.

After the lunch we went with Sommerfeld to the Institute of Theoretical Physics, and then to the Organic Chemical Institute of the Technische Hochschule to visit the great German chemist Hans Fischer (1881–1945).

Next we went to the home of the Rector of the University of Munich for "tea," the quotes being required first because what we actually had was coffee generously laced with brandy, and second because we ended up drinking beer. My companion officer had remarked to the Rector's wife that Bavarian beer was his "weakness"; to which she replied that he must correct his terminology—Bavarian beer must be his "strength." Whereupon she quite naturally ordered up some Löwenbrau.

Back at the Vier Jahreszeiten we had only time to clean up before starting off for dinner at Fajans' home. My respect for my Rockefeller Foundation colleague's intellectual and general fortitude was increased when, after cocktails and a fine dinner with two wines, he entertained Fajans' elderly mother-in-law by reciting Goethe and Schiller to her at length. And, as Pepys remarked on various similar days, so to bed.

This was, to be sure, a gala day with more ceremony than real work; but it does reflect the warmth and friend-liness with which the new young Rockefeller Foundation officer was greeted at all the academic capitals of Europe.

All this was completely fascinating, but it was also hard work. We took many notes and wrote extensive diary every day—or, I should say, every night. One set of such visits did little more than furnish the basis for a continuing series of visits. And, indeed, for my first ten years with the Rockefeller Foundation, I steadily kept repeating these survey tours. During the earlier years the foreign travel was largely confined to Europe, with heavy emphasis on England, Scandinavia, Germany, Switzerland, and France; with somewhat less emphasis on Scotland, Ireland, Holland, Belgium, and Italy; and with occasional trips to Finland, Poland, the Baltic states, Austria, Czechoslovakia, Hungary, and southeastern Europe. Later there were frequent trips to Mexico, Central America, South America (especially Colombia and Brazil); and still later the travel was extended to Turkey, Lebanon, Pakistan, India, Burma, Thailand, Indonesia, the Philippines, Japan, and Hawaii, and to most of the principal regions in Africa south of the Sahara. In between the foreign trips there was an almost constant program of visits to the universities and colleges, big and small, in the United States.

To a person who had previously been teaching mathematics and physics in a Midwestern university in the United States, this kind of program was almost too stimulating. In addition to gradually building up a background of knowledge about scientists and institutions, I had the problem of repairing, at least in part, the deficiencies in my own scientific training.

My conviction that physics and chemistry were ripe for a fruitful union with biology, necessarily somewhat tentative and amateurish when I first accepted the post as a director of the Rockefeller Foundation, steadily became more firm and more enthusiastic as my European visits brought me into contact with scientist after scientist who expressed a desire to participate in our program.

My own training had been, almost exclusively, within the physical sciences. Clearly this was a handicap, both to me and to the program; I earnestly set about trying to minimize the difficulty. Over my first five years I followed a strict program of individual study in the various relevant areas of the biological sciences. I started with genetics, not because I realized in 1932 the key role this subject was destined to play, but at least in part because it is a field congenial to one trained in mathematics. I went at one after another of the areas in which we were working—cellular physiology, organic chemistry, biochemistry, developmental mechanics, the techniques for studying molecular structure, and so on—and did the best I could, subject to the disadvantage of working alone with no laboratory experience, to familiarize myself with the background material.

After World War II, when the National Academy of Sciences sought to produce a series of reports on the biological dangers from radioactive fallout, fifteen of the top geneticists of the United States were chosen to form the committee. But because of some sharp differences of opinion and viewpoint, it was difficult to choose one of these experts as an unbiased chairman of the committee. Because I knew all the men on the committee, and as they felt I was sufficiently familiar with the scientific facts involved, I was asked to serve as chairman. My long years of very amateur study were ridiculously crowned when the press, giving great attention to the report, insisted on referring to me as "the famous geneticist"!

Any division of the Rockefeller Foundation receives a steady stream of requests for aid; and each one of these had to be dealt with responsibly. In the case of any sizable request, this always involved a visit to the institution in question, to study the situation firsthand. As the group of science officers had the steadily accumulating chance to explain the nature of our interest in quantitative experimental biology, we rather rapidly expanded our knowledge of, and our personal acquaintance with, scientists—many of them physicists, biochemists, or organic chemists—who were themselves interested in biological problems.

Although this new Rockefeller Foundation program in quantitative experimental biology was not started until I assumed, in February 1932, my duties as Director of the Division of Natural Sciences, the record of grants indicates that we began rather promptly to find opportunities to finance promising research programs that were relevant to our program interests. In 1932, for example, we made the first of what turned out to be a long series of grants to the

Biological Laboratory at Cold Spring Harbor, Long Island, New York. That institution began a series of summer symposia on quantitative biology, and these meetings played a critically important role in attracting to newer fields of biology a considerable number of brilliant young scientists, several of whom went on to furnish leadership in the new developments. This record is impressively set out in a volume published by the Cold Spring Harbor Laboratory.[2]

Also in 1932 my division of the Rockefeller Foundation made the first of a considerable series of grants to the California Institute of Technology to help support the research program under Dr. Linus Pauling. The Foundation report for 1932, using language that might have seemed a little overoptimistic at that time, stated that Pauling's "program in structural chemistry extends the technique of wave mechanics to the study of complex inorganic and organic molecules."

But in 1951 Dr. Pauling magnificently substantiated that statement by publishing his famous theoretical deduction of the α-helix structure that occurs in proteins, a result which Sir W. Lawrence Bragg has called "the first example of a correct determination of atomic arrangement in biological substances."

Soon after 1932 we began to support the researches of W. T. Astbury in England, a pioneer in the X-ray analysis of natural fibers, his early work being done on wool. And then we began making grants to a considerable number of physicists who were applying X-ray diffraction methods to the study of the structure of biologically important substances, particularly proteins.

I include a few details of the early grants made in the Rockefeller Foundation program for two reasons. First, I consider the emergence of the subject now regularly called molecular biology to be one of the greatest developments in the history of science. The triumphs to date of molecular biology have been largely in the field of genetics. But there is every reason to believe that molecular biology will now attack, and similarly conquer, other basic biological problems—those of immunology, of cellular growth and development (including cancer), and even some of the most basic aspects of the functioning of the central nervous system.

Second, I believe that the support which the Rockefeller Foundation poured into experimental biology over the quarter century following 1932 was vital in encouraging and accelerating and even in initiating the development of molecular biology. Indeed, I think that the most important thing I have ever been able to do was to reorient the Rockefeller Foundation science program in 1932 and direct the strategy of deployment of the large sums which that courageous and imaginative institution made available. It was indeed a large sum, for between 1932 and my retirement from the Rockefeller Foundation in 1959 the total of the grants made in the experimental biology program which I directed was roughly ninety million dollars.

There is some purely factual basis to support the views of the preceding paragraphs. When I read Jim Watson's exciting account[3] of the discovery of the structure of DNA, and came, page after page, to the names of the individuals who had played leading roles, I was struck by the fact that all these names had been written down by me, time after time, in my Rockefeller Foundation diary, and indeed also in recommendations I had made to the Rockefeller Foundation Board of Trustees. As I read on in the Watson book,

I jotted down the names of what seemed to be the most significant actors in the play. I wrote down thirteen names in a first and most important category, and fourteen others, who were somewhat less importantly involved. And of these two lists, every person in the former and more significant group had received assistance from the Rockefeller Foundation. All but three of the second group of fourteen had also received Rockefeller Foundation assistance.

Recently President George W. Beadle of the University of Chicago identified eighteen of the Nobel Laureates, over the period 1954 to 1965, as having been involved in one or another aspect of molecular biology. The mere fact that fifteen of the eighteen had received assistance from the Rockefeller Foundation is not especially significant; for if they are such outstanding scientists it ought to be easy to identify them for aid. So it is much more noteworthy that the Rockefeller Foundation assisted every one of the fifteen before he received the Nobel Prize, and indeed on the average over nineteen years in advance.

Two powerful streams of thought have converged to form the present discipline of molecular biology—the flow of structure studies which recognize physical laws as basic and sufficient for the understanding of the form and function of the parts of a living system, and the considerable flow of studies in the genetics of phage.* The work in phage genetics was to a great extent developed under the leadership of Max Delbrück and his associates. Delbrück was originally trained as a physicist. Watson, one of the two

* Phage—in full, bacteriophage—are viruses that are found in bacteria. In part, at least, because of the simplicity of the host organism, it has been possible to analyze in considerable detail the functions and activities of phage. They may well be the most completely understood of all biological entities.

architects of the structure of DNA, is a biologist originally trained in phage genetics.

To substantiate the claim of the Rockefeller Foundation's influence upon the emergence and development of molecular biology, I have stated some facts about the record of grants to those scientists who led in this development. I can add to this some direct evidence from certain leading recipients of this aid.

Not long ago, I wrote to a number of leading scientists who had been involved in the development of molecular biology, asking for their opinion as to the most satisfactory definition of the phrase "molecular biology," and also raising some questions as to the ways in which this field came into being. In reply, Delbrück wrote me:

"I can only testify as far as I am concerned and here very strongly and unambiguously: without the encouragement of the Rockefeller Foundation received in 1937 and their continuing support through the mid-forties I believe I would hardly have been able to make my contributions to biology." [4]

As part of this same exchange of correspondence about molecular biology, I received a letter from Sir W. Lawrence Bragg, the younger of the father-and-son team that received the Nobel Prize in 1915 for their determinations of crystal structures by X-ray diffraction techniques. In this letter Sir Lawrence said, "concerning the part the Rockefeller Foundation played in helping the 'Cambridge School.' Your help came at a vital time just before the war when I was trying to find some way of supporting Perutz's work [Max F. Perutz was the chairman of the Laboratory of Molecular Biology at Cambridge] and it was continued after it. This school was responsible for DNA, for the first protein structures, for the first understanding of virus structure, and for work on muscle. The extent to which the X-ray analysis of protein was pioneer work is shown by the fact that only now, twelve years after the trail was beaten at Cambridge and the Royal Institution, has any other research centre succeeded in getting a protein 'out.' I am allowing myself to put this so strongly just because I think that the Foundation's help made an outstanding difference to these advances." Perutz has also written me, ". . . the Cambridge work on the structure of large molecules would never have got off the ground but for the Foundation's support."

The Rockefeller Foundation has, I firmly believe, a solid and authoritative basis for taking satisfaction in the role it played in emphasizing, over a period of over a quarter of a century, the support of research in quantitative biology.

6. The War Years

Extensive travel in Europe and many contacts with the Jewish refugee problem had convinced me, over the 1930s, that something evil was taking place in Germany. In spite of all my theoretical persuasion that war is no way to solve the world's problems, I became even more convinced that the United States would have to become involved. So dominant and compelling was this judgment that I concluded, in the spring of 1940, that I must try to find some way of being personally useful. This was some eighteen months before the attack on Pearl Harbor; but I knew that a few national leaders in science, and notably Vannevar Bush, had already been thinking and planning about ways in which the scientific resources of the country could be brought to bear upon the problems of warfare.

The National Academy of Sciences was created in 1863, during the Civil War, to make available to the government the best scientific advice available. By the time of World War I, the Academy had quite naturally taken on a broad range of responsibilities not at all closely associated with warfare, so it was then necessary for President Wilson to request the President of the National Academy to set up a new affiliated organization, the National Research Council, to stimulate research and to aid in the application of all science to the problems of war. The NRC was the principal agency that brought science to bear on World War I.

History then repeated itself. By 1940 the National Research Council had become so deeply engaged in the programs it had developed over the preceding twenty-year period that clearly a new organization, flexible and un-committed, must again be set up. Vannevar Bush was then chairman of the National Advisory Committee for Aeronautics, a group that had shown what could be done in a field strategic to national defense, and he was also president of the Carnegie Institution of Washington, an organization with varied scientific interests. He was a highly respected scientist-engineer, with wide acquaintance. He had energy, imagination, and courage. It was natural and, as it turned out, exceedingly fortunate that President Roosevelt asked the Council of National Defense to enlist Bush as the head of a National Defense Research Committee (a year later to be called the OSRD—the Office of Scientific Research and Development—this latter being a more accurate title, as it had become clear that the organization would be involved not only in research but also in the practical stages of construction and testing of pilot models).

As soon as I heard the news about this new organization, I wrote to Bush, telling him that I was anxious to be of some service and that I was prepared to take on a full-time job. As a result of this offer, I was one of the first appointees to Bush's new organization. And I was asked to take charge of organizing and directing a section of the OSRD called the fire-control section.

As used by the military, "fire control" refers to all the devices and procedures used to assure that any "projectile" (a shell fired from an anti-aircraft gun, a bomb dropped from an airplane, or a torpedo launched against a ship) will in fact hit the desired target.

During the course of the war the fire-control division of OSRD was concerned with the design and test of devices for all of these varied uses, but a big part of our effort was concerned with "ground-to-air" fire; that is, the equipment controlling ground-based anti-aircraft guns, which may be anything from 50-caliber machine guns up to the 90-millimeter rifles whose targets are high-flying aircraft.

To hit an enemy airplane you have to know where it is and how it is moving, so that you can calculate where it will be by the time the shell reaches it. The equipment that furnishes the data about position and motion of the target can be called the tracking mechanism. This mechanism utilizes both optical and electrical means (radar), the latter procedure involving the sending of a pulse of electrical energy which is reflected by the enemy plane back down to the tracking equipment, which then computes the distance to the plane from the time required for the pulse to make the round trip to the plane and back.

There must be sophisticated and rapid equipment usually called a "director" or a "predictor" which calculates where the target plane will be when the projectile gets there, and which also calculates just how the anti-aircraft gun should be pointed and when it should be fired.

This calculation must take into account not only the characteristics of the target's motion but also the ballistic path of the shells, as influenced by wind and air density at different levels. Since the guns are heavy, there must be powerful equipment, controlled by the predictor, which continuously adjusts the orientation of the gun.

When we came on the scene, the Navy had comparatively advanced devices to carry out the functions of fire control, their equipment involving gyroscopic stabilization to take care of the roll and pitch of the vessel, rapid computation, and automatic power control of the guns. The Army, however, had equipment that had hardly been improved since World War I and was useless in handling the heights and speeds of World War II targets.

It is not surprising that anti-aircraft fire, using the then existing equipment, was ineffective. The bombing of England began on July 10, 1940 (the very day on which I had the first conference about my new task with Vannevar Bush), and in October 1940 it was estimated that at least 10,000 rounds of fire from 3-inch anti-aircraft guns were expended for each plane shot down in the London area. Even that figure, moreover, is almost certainly too low.

My first move, after a long conference with Bush in which he outlined the array of problems and opportunities as he saw them, was the selection of a group of key associates, and in that selection I was fortunate indeed—or expertly advised, or both. I have never enjoyed working with a large "committee," and I originally chose only three persons as the core of our organization. They were—alphabetically listed for I could not possibly assign any priorities— Samuel H. Caldwell, then a professor of electrical engineering at MIT who had been associated with Bush in the development of electrical and mechanical computing devices; Thornton Carl Fry, the head of the mathematics group at the Bell Telephone Laboratories and an extremely clearheaded person with imagination as well as knowledge of the analytical theory and the practical construction of all types of electrical devices; and Edward J. Poitras. Ed was

—and is—a man of very special personal and professional qualifications who at that time had most recently been engaged in designing the automatic control system for the 200-inch telescope on Mount Palomar—a pointing problem which, except for the vast differences in angular velocities, has many similarities with gun-pointing problems. Ed knew gyroscope theory and practice, and was extraordinarily gifted and ingenious in his knowledge of all sorts of control procedures. To our central committee we soon added Duncan J. Stewart, then the chief engineer of the Barber-Coleman Company of Rockford, Illinois, a concern with special skill in the design and construction of intricate precision devices as well as in control engineering. This control committee we supplemented, as the work progressed, with a considerable group of full-time technical aides, each especially chosen for a particular line, with an extensive group of consultants, largely drawn from engineering industries. The actual projects were ordinarily carried out under contract with engineering firms.

It is a tragic shame that peace seems to offer almost no challenge that will evoke the best from men, but war, horrid and cruel as it is, often brings out the highest qualities of everyone.

We met the most dedicated cooperation in universities and in many technical industries. In the case of the various branches of the armed services we were initially—and quite understandably—met by the attitude, "NDRC, what is that and who are you?" After all, we were raw amateurs, meeting men who were lifetime professionals.

There were numerous groups and military and industrial agencies with which we had to establish working relations, from whom we had to learn what needed to be done, and with whom we had to explore the possibilities where we might be useful.

Certain major facts emerged fairly promptly: that for the Army the problem of small-arms fire was both more difficult and less pressing than the problem of furnishing good fire control for a weapon capable of shooting down high planes—say the 90-millimeter rifle which was by that time scheduled to replace the older 3-inch weapon; that the Air Corps was pretty content with its Norden bomb sight, and was not yet ready to worry much about plane-to-plane fire. Indeed, about the only way at that time for a fighter plane to shoot down an enemy plane was to outfly and outmaneuver him, getting so close on his tail that all the pilot had to do was pull the trigger. Plane-to-ground problems, and the defense of big bombers against fighters, were to come later.

We carried out various analytical studies and practical tests which showed that the mechanical methods (gears and cams) that had previously been used in directors or predictors would be neither rapid enough nor accurate enough to cope with the fast targets of World War II. At just the moment when it was obvious that a brand-new approach would be necessary, the Bell Telephone Laboratories came forward with the proposal that they develop an electrical gun director. The original concept of this novel device had occurred to one of their engineers, D. B. Parkinson, in a dream!

Mervin L. Kelly, director of research at the Bell Telephone Laboratories, had proposed the development of this instrument to the Ordnance Department but had been rebuffed. He asked Fry whether the OSRD would consider backing the idea. It was, at that moment, not at all clear that the proposed electrical director would be either as rapid or as accurate as the existing mechanical directors; for its computation process relied on various electrical devices of novel and unproven design. But the electrical instrument could be produced in large numbers by relatively unskilled labor, whereas the Sperry type required precision machine tools and machine-tool skills. Thornton Fry therefore decided to recommend the project to our group.

On October 24, 1940, we had our first conference at the Bell Telephone Laboratories, and their group outlined their thinking about an electrical gun director or predictor.

On November 4 I had a meeting with the officers of the Technical Staff, Army Ordnance. It was my task to sell the idea of an electrical predictor to a group unacquainted with the techniques involved and traditionally skeptical about the use under battle conditions of anything "electrical." However, the meeting concluded with a decision to request the NDRC to proceed, to be responsible for financing, and to take full charge of all technical supervision and direction.

From that moment on we kept in closest touch with the BTL group. We assisted their contacts with various service groups, obtained data for them, and held frequent conferences with them at which all the aspects of their design and plans were thoroughly discussed.

Throughout 1941 we had long monthly conferences at the Bell Telephone Laboratories. We acted, on a continuous schedule, as the link between the Bell Labs group and the U.S. and British service authorities, as well as all the other scientists, engineers, and industrial groups interested in the director problem.

By September 1941, a first model was being assembled.

On November 3 an "open house" was held at the Bell Labs. To call it "open" is a misnomer; for the development was of course carried out under closest secrecy. The select group invited was told: "Overalls will be worn. Bring your own connecting clips. Lubricating oil will be served at 4:30 p.m." On November 29 the electrical gun director went to the Coast Artillery Board at Fort Monroe for test.

There were, of course, preliminary difficulties when the instrument was first tested. This was a brand-new device, involving many novel parts. Minor errors turned up in the tests and had to be corrected. A major problem was the design of suitable "smoothing circuits" to average out the inevitable fluctuations in the input data. But in February 1942, the instrument was accepted by the Army, and its experimental designation as T-10 was changed to the production label M-9.

This was by no means the only director project which Section D-2 set up and supervised. A number of novel ideas came to the surface and were tried out. At the Bell Labs itself another design, using a different coordinate system and capable of predicting along curved flight paths, was given a great deal of attention. All this was necessary insurance, although the alternative designs were never used.

To go on with the M-9 story: On June 12, 1944, the first German "buzz bombs," the V-1's, began to rain down terror on London. These were small pilot-less aircraft— or as we say now, missiles—preset when launched to descend and detonate in the London area. By this time three American developments, all carried out under the OSRD, had progressed to the point of practical service. A number of U.S. 90-millimeter anti-aircraft batteries with automatic power controls were installed on the east coast of England.

Radar equipment developed by another section of the OSRD carried out automatic tracking of the enemy "planes" (in this case, the buzz bombs), and furnished the data about location and flight path. The BTL director M-9 accepted these data and computed the predicted position. The fuse-time settings did not have to be utilized, for by then still another OSRD development was available for use, the proximity fuse. This device, developed under the inspired direction of the physicist Merle Tuve (his section of the OSRD was so clearly a personal affair that it was designated as Section "T"), was an electrical marvel that replaced the time fuse in the nose of the shells and automatically detonated them when they came into the near neighborhood of the target.

The success of these three interdependent devices, the radar set, the electrical director, and the proximity fuse, is a matter of record. As of August 2, 1944, before the U.S. batteries become operative, the cumulative averages on destructions of V-1 were that, of those launched, anti-aircraft fire destroyed 10 per cent. After the five battalions of U.S. 90-millimeter guns were installed, equipped with automatic radar tracking, the M-9 director, and proximity fuses, the percentage of buzz bombs destroyed by A.A. fire rose by a factor of five, to 50 per cent. Actually the shooting record was better than this average figure indicates. Of the V-1's actually *engaged* by the heavy A.A., the percentage of kills was about 80. For example, the U.S. 124th and 125th Battalions, during one period, destroyed thirty-one of forty that were launched over their area. One battery, observed by Clarence A. Lovell of Bell Telephone Laboratories, who made a trip there engaged nine buzz bombs, all of which were shot down.

Warren Weaver (left) with his older brother, Paul John, and their mother; (below) the Weaver family bicycling. Reedsburg, Wisconsin, about 1897.

A Rockefeller Foundation study group in an experimental wheat field in Mexico, 1949: (left to right) William I. Myers, dean of agriculture, Cornell University; Thomas Parran, former U.S. surgeon general; Weaver; John S. Dickey, president of Dartmouth College.

Mariachis in a Mexican village serenading Foundation officials Chester I. Barnard, president (center), and Weaver (fourth from left), and Mexican Senator Antonio Ramos Millan (second from left), 1949. (© Ignacio Sanchez Mendoza)

Weaver with Nazario Ortiz Garza, Mexican minister of agriculture, 1949.

Planning the dedication of Warren Weaver Hall, Courant Institute of Mathematical Sciences, New York University, 1961: (left to right) Weaver; Alfred P. Sloan, Jr.; Richard Courant. (New York University)

Breaking ground for the Hall, 1962: (center, with spade) Courant; (behind Courant, left to right) Weaver; James M. Hester, president, New York University; Sloan; James J. Stoker, director, Courant Institute; George D. Stoddard, executive vice president, New York University. (New York University)

Warren Weaver Hall, 1965. (New York University)

With Edward A. Carlson, president, Pacific Science Center Foundation, under the arches for which the Arches of Science Award was named. Seattle, Washington, 1965. (Dudley, Hardin & Yang, Inc.)

Dael Wolfle, executive officer of the American Association for the Advancement of Science, presenting Weaver with the gold medal of the Foundation's first Arches of Science Award, Seattle, 1965. (Barton L. Attebery)

At a reception for Joseph E. Slater, new president of The Salk Institute for Biological Studies, LaJolla, California, 1968: (left to right) Slater, Mrs. Slater, Weaver, Mrs. Weaver. (D. K. Miller, The Salk Institute)

South Laboratory, The Salk Institute, LaJolla, 1968. (D. K. Miller, The Salk Institute)

At the Sloan Foundation, 1961. (New York University, William R. Simmons)

Roughly 300 M-9's were landed in France on D-Day, being floated ashore in waterproof packages. One M-9 floated out to sea and had to be sunk by our own naval shellfire. In operation on the beach, on $D + 1$, a battery engaged three targets and shot down two. The performance in France set completely new records for anti-aircraft fire.

On August 12, 1944, General Sir Frederick A. Pile, in charge of the British anti-aircraft command, wrote to General George Marshall a letter referring to the destruction of buzz bombs (our division was sent a copy) which said in part, "The equipment you have sent us is absolutely first class, and every day we are getting better results with it. . . . We are employing the SCR 584* with the BTL predictor. This predictor is also an outstanding job. . . . Finally there is the fuse which is so secret that I can only describe it by its nickname in this country, 'Bonzo'. . . . Our percentage of 'kills' is not high enough, but the curve is going up at a nice pace. . . . As the troops get more expert with the equipment I have no doubt very few bombs will reach London. . . . All this is due in the first place to you for sending us the equipment, and then to the extraordinarily skilled designers and the many fine workmen who had a hand in producing three of the most outstanding A.A. equipments of the war."

I have devoted considerable space to the account of the design and development of a successful electrical anti-aircraft predictor, because this was one of the largest and most useful of the projects sponsored by the fire-control section of OSRD.

However, we were involved in dozens of other projects with special emphasis on the sighting systems used to direct

*The official designation of the automatic radar tracker.

the guns of an airplane against enemy aircraft, and on equipment which made possible accurate and realistic testing of fire-control equipment. We had rather special success with the design of a bomb sight for use in low-level attacks on submarines. A thousand of these sights were built, of which half went to the Atlantic Fleet and half to the British.

Long after the war, Poitras, in France on a business trip, was talking to an official of Air France. Reminiscing about war days, the Frenchman explained that he had served with the Free French forces, and as a bombing pilot had operated out of Oran and Dakar with American B-24 planes, hunting subs. "Did you have any kills?" Poitras asked. "But yes, m'sieur, with the magnificent sight I had, it was impossible to miss." Poitras went on to ask about this sight—did it have this, did it operate thus? The Frenchman, more and more amazed, finally asked how his American friend could possibly know so much about the sight. "Well, you see," said Poitras, "I designed it."

By 1942 it had become evident that the activities of the fire-control section were developing along two rather different directions, one concerned with the design and production of "hardware"—i.e., actual operating devices of various sorts, and the other concerned primarily with the mathematical analysis of problems, this involving paper rather than hardware.

The problems we worked on sometimes related to, and were preliminary to, the design of devices; often they related to the optimum employment of devices; and sometimes they were of still broader character, concerned with tactical or even strategic plans.

As the war went on, the emphasis on the design and production of hardware necessarily tapered off somewhat, for the practical reason that by then a brand-new device simply could not be conceived of, designed, built in pilot model, tested, improved, standardized, and put into service in time to affect the conduct of the war. On the other hand, the demands to carry out analytical studies kept increasing rapidly.

In the summer of 1942 we had had to recruit more and more mathematicians in order to keep up with the demands on us. And by the late fall of 1942, Dr. Bush and his colleagues heading up the OSRD carried out a reorganization which shifted the fire-control problems to a new Division 7 and created a new OSRD agency called AMP, or Applied Mathematics Panel. This panel was asked to be of general assistance in connection with analytical and mathematical problems, not only for Division 7 but for all the other divisions of OSRD as well—even more broadly, for the services and the war effort. I was continued as a member of the new Division 7, and was there placed in charge of the analytical aspects of fire-control problems; and I was made the chief of the Applied Mathematics Panel. The new Division 7 was headed by Harold L. Hazen, then head of Electrical Engineering at MIT and later Dean of the Graduate School.

The Applied Mathematics Panel was relatively small, consisting of the mathematicians Richard Courant, Griffith Conrad Evans, Thornton Carl Fry, Lawrence Murray Graves, Harold Marston Morse, Oswald Veblen, and Samuel Stanley Wilks. They were officially known as the "Committee Advisory to the Scientific Officer," that being myself. We also had the incomparably fine assistance of Dr. Mina

Rees as chief technical aide. We sponsored and directed the work of several hundred other mathematicians. Many of these were men whose primary interests were in the purest of pure mathematics but who were unselfishly willing to devote themselves, during the war, to very specific applied problems. The roster included a good number of the ablest mathematicians of our country. We also were fortunate in recruiting a number of men highly skilled in statistical techniques although not professionally classified as mathematicians. Notable among this latter group were W. Allen Wallis, now president of the University of Rochester, and Milton Friedman, now holding a distinguished professorship of economics at the University of Chicago.

To those unfamiliar with the power of mathematical analysis, it may seem strange that there were so many demands on the Applied Mathematics Panel from the different branches of the armed services.

Some of our studies were of the "operations research" type, furnishing a guide as to how certain military actions could most effectively be carried out—for example, what kind of bombing attack had the best chance of clearing a safe passage through a mined area; how a multiple salvo of torpedos should be aimed to have the highest probability of hitting an enemy vessel carrying out evasive action; what flight pattern for a group of bombers would minimize the probability that shots fired at attacking enemy fighter planes would inflict damage to our own planes.

Under the auspices of the Applied Mathematics Panel were developed powerful new statistical techniques which improved the efficiency and lowered the cost of testing our own war matériel. In just one such instance, involving improved testing of the propellant for rockets, the financial saving—not to mention the improvement in the matériel —was so great that within a few months it was sufficient to pay the cost of the total program of the Applied Mathematics Panel throughout the war.

The whole kaleidoscopic pattern of activity of the Applied Mathematics Panel does not easily lend itself to condensed description. We set up, carried through, and reported on a total of 194 studies. They were summarized, after the war, in four published volumes.

I have postponed to the end of this chapter the report of a period that chronologically belongs near the beginning. Early in 1941 it became clear to the officials of Dr. Bush's OSRD that close contact must be established with the British military experts and with the English scientists, so many of whom were by then devoting their energies and abilities to the war. President Roosevelt accordingly appointed an official scientific mission. The first group to go, on February 15, was headed by James B. Conant and included Carroll Wilson (for a time the general manager of the Atomic Energy Commission and now a professor at MIT) and Frederick L. Hovde (now president of Purdue University). When Conant and Wilson returned to the United States, Hovde stayed on as the permanent secretary of the mission.

The second group to go, following soon after the first, consisted of Dr. Kenneth T. Bainbridge, physicist at Harvard, Ed Poitras, and myself.

We sailed on March 3 on the *Sibony*, a rickety and dirty old wreck that was leased to the American Export Lines by the "Cuba Mail," the designation assigned to the

Ward Line after the *Morro Castle* tragedy had removed whatever luster the original company name had previously possessed. The ship had been decommissioned, presumably as unfit; but under the demands of war she was again, albeit somewhat dubiously, in service. The trip to Lisbon, with a stopover at Bermuda, was tedious, uncomfortable, and unpleasant. Ed and I threatened to move from our cabin to the nearby men's toilet, which was warmer and smelled better.

We arrived in Lisbon on March 14, and there had a three-day delay before flying to England.

From the very first, our stay in England was delightful and rewarding, for we were so warmly accepted and assisted by British scientists, many of whom I had come to know on my Rockefeller Foundation visits to England, and because we were given every conceivable assistance by top military authorities. We were able to meet and discuss problems with all the military, technical, and scientific personnel responsible for anti-aircraft and other fire-control problems. We were at Portsmouth, Plymouth, Exeter, and other frequently attacked locations on the vulnerable south coast. We went to Aberporth in Wales, where rocket research was going forward, and also to Swansea. We made short visits to Cambridge and Oxford. At Cambridge, where few incendiaries fell, one landed on the roof of the famed Cavendish Laboratory, fell through, and landed plop in a sink where it harmlessly burned out! We had an impressive session with the Ordnance Board, an organization with representation from the Army, Navy, and Air, originally set up in the fifteenth century.

We had one night with an anti-aircraft battery on the outskirts of London. And on the night of April 16, 1941, we had the stimulating but somewhat dubious pleasure of sitting out the worst night of bombing that London experienced throughout the war. The raid started before nine in the evening and lasted until after five in the morning. It was estimated that between 500 and 1,000 German bombers were over London that night, and about fifty bombs fell in the close vicinity of Grosvenor House, where we were staying. From the roof of our hotel one saw a ring of huge fires, over toward the City, the Cheapside area, and the East India Docks.

But the next morning everyone was calmly and efficiently at work, bringing all the fires under control so that they would not furnish directing targets for the next night, and re-establishing electric, water, and phone service.

The total picture, as eventually recalled, is made up of a large number of small vignettes, each itself unimportant. There was, for example, the night at dinner when I asked the waiter for some mustard with my lamb. It was a tense night, but his traditions did not waver. Very politely but firmly he said, "It is, sir, very unorthodox with lamb, but I will bring it."

One night we were staying—the only Americans—in a country inn not far from London. We arrived after "closing time" but an exception was made and the Americans were given a drink. We were at once accepted by all the persons in the lounge, and Anglo-American relations were toasted all around with vigor and friendly warmth. Soon one of the wives, who had been upstairs tucking in her five-year-old son, rejoined the group and said, "I think you should know what just happened. I told my small son there were two Americans downstairs, and he said, 'Mummy, did you remember to thank the American gentlemen for the big bombers?' " The next morning we even had five prunes apiece and a small piece of bacon with our egg.

One day, at lunch in a pub with officers from a nearby military establishment, one of them told us of a toy automobile-rocket contest some officers recently ran. Each team of two was allowed to spend up to a shilling for the automobile, to which they would lash a small toy rocket. All the contestants would be lined up on the side of a tennis court, the rockets lit, and the first toy auto across the court won the grand prize. He and his companion went to the big toy store on Regent Street—Hamley's—and asked to see toy automobiles. The first one the girl showed them cost thirty-five guineas! They gradually backed her down to cheaper and cheaper ones, and finally one of the officers smiled and said to the girl, "But Mummy said I wasn't to spend over a shilling." They finally got a cheap enough model, and spent the rest of the afternoon trying it out in Regent's Park, to the considerable irritation of the park policemen.

On the plane down to Portugal, starting our way back to our warm, safe homes, I wrote in my diary:

"I am moved to pay my tribute to the qualities of the average working-class Englishman. . . . The morning after our big blitz our waiter came in, with our rolls and coffee, cheerful as ever; and when we inevitably turned to talking of the raid it developed that from twelve to three in the morning he had been up on the roof 'spotting,' fully exposed to the whole direct terror of that flaming night. We later got out of him that his home had been bombed some months ago, that a shell splinter had gone right through the only suits he owned, and that the roof caved in and it rained steadily for the three days which intervened before the authorities dared allow him to re-enter his house. But for all these things he had only a shrug and a smile. He was touchingly appreciative when we gave him a suit, an overcoat, and a pair of shoes; and at eight o'clock that night he was still on duty and still smiling. There are millions of such people in England today, carrying great burdens with modest gallantry.'

7. Postwar Activities

During the war period my responsibilities to Dr. Bush's OSRD had first claim on my time, and in fact demanded practically all of my energy. I did, nevertheless, maintain regular contact with what was going on in the Rockefeller Foundation.

And immediately after the war I began to devote a good deal of my time to a Rockefeller Foundation activity that had, in fact, been initiated in 1941; and I must interrupt the chronological order to go back and recount the beginnings of that activity.

During his presidency of the Rockefeller Foundation, it was a custom of Raymond B. Fosdick, who was always on the alert to pick up ideas, to lunch and talk with a wide variety of experienced persons. On such an occasion in 1941 he talked with Henry A. Wallace, then Vice President of the United States. Wallace had just returned from a trip to Mexico—I think, his first—and as an agricultural expert, well acquainted with the lush acres of hybrid corn in the Midwest, he had been disturbed, if not indeed shocked, to see the sparse rows of poor corn in Mexico. Had it been later in the season, he would have been even more troubled by the small ears, scarcely ever more than one to a stalk.

He remarked that if anyone could increase the yield

per acre of corn and beans in Mexico, it would contribute more effectively to the welfare of the country and the happiness of its people than anything else. Fosdick recalled Wallace's remark as "a casual comment"; but it was not treated casually.

Directly after his return from Washington Fosdick dropped into my office, told me of Wallace's remark, and asked, "Is there anything we can do about this?"

"I don't know," I said, "but I know how we can find out."

For the immediate steps, and for much of the detailed guidance until the war was over, I had to depend upon my fellow officers in the Division of Natural Sciences. These were Frank B. Hanson and Harry M. Miller, Jr. Both had been trained as biologists, both had had extensive foreign assignments, both were outstandingly loyal, dedicated, and intelligent. They were thoroughly seasoned foundation officers, each with nearly twenty years' experience.

Since they were at that time the two natural-science officers on full duty in the New York office, all moves in the agricultural program were discussed between them. And it is of special importance that, as a colleague officer in the sister foundation, the General Education Board, they had the specifically relevant advice of Albert R. Mann, who for many years had been Dean of the College of Agriculture at Cornell University.

In the Rockefeller Foundation there is a strongly rooted tradition that the best initial step in approaching any problem is to get the advice of experts, to take the necessary time, and to remain discreetly silent until there is something to report.

The first decision, therefore, was to select a small group

of experts to go to Mexico, spend many weeks there, travel through all the varied agricultural regions, see what was limiting the production of their principal crops, and come to a judgment as to whether and how the foundation might be of aid. Three men were chosen, and their skill, wisdom, and method were such that the Rockefeller Foundation has insisted that all three of them remain associated with the program ever since, as consultants and for a wide variety of short-term assignments. It well illustrates the way Hanson, Miller, and Mann operated that one of the three men chosen for the Mexico survey, the soils specialist Richard Bradfield of Cornell, was nominated by Mann, the geneticist and plant breeder Paul Manglesdorf of Harvard was nominated by Hanson, and the plant pathologist Elvin C. Stakman of the University of Minnesota was nominated by Miller.

There was no publicity given to this preliminary investigation; and indeed after the three experts submitted their report, which indicated in some detail what could be done and how, there was a second and longer unpublicized period of preparation. For two things had to be accomplished or the work could not possibly succeed. First, the proposal had to be skillfully suggested to a number of Mexican officials in such a way that they totally embraced the idea as something they themselves desired. That delicate piece of negotiation was carried out by Miller. A skilled linguist, with long and successful experience in dealing with the Latin mind and temperament, he was ideal for this job.

Second, and as is critically true of any project, the scheme would never be any better than its leadership, so we were determined to get the best. We did, as events have clearly proved. J. George Harrar was, at that moment, the head of the department of plant pathology at Washington State College. He had spent several years as professor of botany at the University of Puerto Rico, and both he and his wife were fluent in Spanish. Besides his technical and professional qualifications, George had been a four-letter athlete at Oberlin, and when he eventually became the head of the Mexican–North American agricultural group in Mexico he furnished them leadership at every level—he could run faster, jump a wider stream, dance the samba better, shoot better, and work harder both in the office and in the field than any one. In tact and courtesy, in skill and knowledge, in his infectious personality, in energy and dedication, he was the ideal leader. That Harrar is now the president of the Rockefeller Foundation is but the natural culmination of a plot that some of us schemed in 1941.

The Mexican agricultural program was to be a collaborative one. The Mexican government was to furnish the necessary land, and was to offer the cooperation of its own agricultural groups; but the Rockefeller Foundation would itself furnish the direction, the scientific staff, and the necessary tools, equipment, and supplies. The idea was to create in Mexico a first-rate, thoroughly modern agricultural research and development group that could focus all the power of modern methods on the problems of improving the principal food crops of Mexico. This meant breeding new varieties of corn, beans, and wheat to obtain plants suitable for Mexican soil and climate. Also involved was control of pests and diseases, modernizing horticultural methods, improving the soil used for crop production, and determining what fertilization practices were suitable for Mexico. Most important of all, however, was the basic training and eventually the advanced education of literally hundreds of Mexican young men, so that the program could year after year become more Mexican in its management.

The young North American agricultural scientists who were selected to go to Mexico in this program were chosen with the greatest care—for the human characteristics of the men and their wives as well as for their technical proficiency. They were taken on a permanent basis and given ample opportunity, with study leaves and trips to scientific meetings, to continue their professional progress. All became proficient in Spanish, and the families entered into the culture of their new home.

The turnover on the Rockefeller Foundation agricultural staff has been phenomenally low. The men have been much sought after, by industries and by great universities. One did leave for a time—on a very good job—but is now back in a high position. Another who left became a university president, but is now back directing an agricultural program in the Orient.

When I recommended to the Rockefeller Board of Trustees, early in the 1940s, the first appropriation in support of the Mexican program, I tried to be realistic about the difficulties we faced: We would have droughts, floods, diseases. Promising developments would undoubtedly prove faulty. Progress would be slow and hard. So I asked the trustees not to approve the first appropriation unless they were prepared to be patient with little progress during ten years of a twenty-five-year span. That span has passed, and the support of the trustees is as steady and enthusiastic as ever.

Another type of patience recognizes that a great program need not start with a splurge. For 1942 the total expenditure in the Mexican agricultural program was under

$2,000. In 1943 it rose to slightly over $13,000. The next year it was over $40,000, and by 1945 it was nearly $100,000. Ten years later, in 1955, the whole agricultural program of the Rockefeller Foundation (by then extended to Colombia and Chile), including supporting grants and the essential costs of scholarships and fellowships, was pushing $2 million annually. Four years after that the figure was $5.5 million. This kind of increase, growing as one learns how to grow, is what gets results.

Once the war was over, confident that the program in experimental biology had developed sufficient momentum to roll on, I devoted much time and energy to the New York office administration of the agricultural program. I could think of nothing that then seemed more important to me than to see that the men in the field—Mexico, Colombia, Chile, and later India—were sympathetically and efficiently backed and provided for in the home office. And with George Harrar I began, directly after the war, to make frequent trips to the locations of the agricultural activity— first to Mexico, and then as the program expanded, to the other sites. The work in Mexico prospered, and in 1950 a similar operating program was opened up in Colombia; and in 1955 another, though smaller, in Chile. Other Central and South American countries learned about the success of the work, and although no further formal operating programs were started in that area, cooperative arrangements were set up in various locations, and money grants were made to aid agricultural progress. Thus the travel involved Central America, Ecuador, Peru, Argentina, and Brazil, as well as the locations of the operating programs.

Indeed in the early 1950s it was clear that important results were being achieved throughout Central and South

America. Corn and wheat were raised very generally through all this region, and potatoes (a strategic crop) were a favored food all up and down the Andean ridge. Effort was expanded through a Central American Corn Improvement Program that led eventually to the establishment of an International Maize and Wheat Improvement Center, created in Mexico through the cooperation of the Rockefeller Foundation and the Mexican government. Improved varieties of wheat, bred in Mexico, have by now been introduced successfully in Libya, the Sudan, Kenya, Rhodesia, Jordan, Israel, Afghanistan, Pakistan, India, and Nepal as well as in many South American countries. The improved corns have been similarly introduced in a large number of countries—Nepal, Pakistan, Malaysia, Kenya, Ethiopia, and the United Arab Republic, for example.

In 1952 Harrar and I went to India, and explored with the leaders there the possibility that the foundation establish a cooperative agricultural program in India, to improve the yields and qualities of the wheat, corn, sorghum, millet, and other grains that were a vital part of their food supply. This was followed by another long trip to India and the Far East in 1953; and in 1954 the first appropriations were made in support of the Indian program. The development occurred rapidly, for by then the foundation had a reservoir of trained personnel, of improved plant materials, and of experience.

On the 1953 trip, which included the countries of the great Far Eastern crescent, one tip of which is in Japan and one in Pakistan, Harrar and I were greatly impressed by the returns that might be realized from a concentrated study of rice. "Rice is the most important food in the world.

Although surpassed by wheat in the world's total acreage, the volume of food produced by the world rice crop is 10 to 20 per cent greater than that of wheat." [1] For about 60 per cent of the world's population, something like 80 per cent of the calorie intake comes from rice.

When we returned to New York, Harrar and I wrote a report for our fellow officers and for the trustees in which we pointed out: "Rice is . . . the major food for those parts of the world which are underprivileged, and where the race between food and population is so grim that starvation is a constant threat and a not infrequent reality. Any useful knowledge concerning rice thus bears upon the major food needs of some one and a half billion people, many of whom constitute the world's hungriest and most precariously fed group."

Although rice has fed millions for thousands of years, it is nevertheless a striking fact that at the time of our report strangely little was known about it. This was partly because rice has been important in those parts of the world where science has not progressed very rapidly, but also because the rice plant is, speaking roughly, too good for its own good. It is so vigorous, so able to cope with a variety of conditions, and so resistant to many diseases that it manages to produce a tolerable crop under almost any circumstances.

In various places, and notably in Japan, there had been able and vigorous programs of research on the more obvious and applied aspects of rice cultivation: what fertilizer to apply and when, the effect of depth of paddy water, selection of the most promising varieties, and so on. In a very few places, and notably at Cuttack in India, there had been recent attempts to cross the high-yielding Japonica types with the Indica types that prosper in the tropical latitudes; and at Cuttack a beginning had also been made on basic studies of the rice plant.

But generally speaking, at the time of our report, many fundamental questions about the rice plant could only be answered with "No one knows."

This 1954 report went on to analyze the value and the desirable structure of an international rice research program. There were, especially at that time, grave problems concerning the suitable location for an international rice research center. The countries with scientific strength to offer were Japan and India. For a variety of reasons, a location more in the center of the great rice crescent seemed desirable. But certain political resentments, left over from World War II, complicated the problem. We did, however, strongly recommend that the Rockefeller Foundation study the problem and undertake, as soon as possible, the establishment of such an activity. Two specialists were added to the foundation staff, and they spent eighteen months in the Orient, becoming familiar with the institutions, individuals, research, and extension programs concerned there with crop improvement. It was not until 1962 that the groundwork had been laid for the actual launching of the program; and at that time the International Rice Research Institute was created. The Ford Foundation, long conversant with the successes elsewhere of the Rockefeller Foundation agricultural activities, offered to cooperate in the venture. They furnished more than $11 million to create the entire physical plant required, and generously agreed to share with the Rockefeller Foundation the annual budgets for at least seven years. The research center was located at Los Baños in

the Philippines, and an entire community was created—
laboratories, library, field buildings and equipment, and
housing for the staff. All this was done with the warm cooperation of the Philippine government, which furnished
the land. The Rockefeller Foundation took the responsibility for the staffing and scientific direction.

This institute has already had outstanding successes.
A short-stemmed, stiff-strawed variety of rice has been bred
and released to interested governments; and gains of 50 to
200 per cent in yield have been reported from locations in
India, Pakistan, Thailand, the Philippines, and even in
Latin America. One hundred and six scholars and thirty-five
fellows from sixteen countries have received in-service training at this institute in the past four years. Newspapers,
magazines, movies, and television have been publicizing
the great importance to the world's food problem of "the
new rice," now regularly referred to as the "miracle rice."

When one spends years on a job involving a mass of
almost daily detail and a multitude of projects, he is fortunate if, looking back, he has the satisfaction of having been
associated with one or two activities that have had sizable,
successful, and permanent impact. For my nearly thirty
years in the Rockefeller Foundation, I have that sort of
satisfaction with respect to two programs, in both of which
I had the privilege of major administrative responsibility:
the program in experimental biology which played a significant role in initiating and developing the present-day
field of molecular biology; and the agricultural program.
An editorial, referring especially to the dwarf wheat
strain developed in Mexico and the improved rice strains
developed at Los Baños, stated, "They have provided coun-

tries which were perennially faced with starvation with the means not only to become self-sufficient, but equally important, to regain their self-respect and national pride." [2]

The Rockefeller Foundation's agricultural program is widely recognized as a great example of what can be accomplished when a superbly competent technical staff, dedicated to long-range effort, is given wise direction and is sustained by stable planning and ample support. The primary credit must go to the leadership of George Harrar.

Under Harrar's presidency the program of the Rockefeller Foundation has been reorganized to furnish approaches to five problems of world-wide importance. All those who were associated with the early stages, a quarter century ago, take deep satisfaction that one of the five problems chosen for increased future emphasis is headed: "Towards the Conquest of Hunger."

Before the war, I had had close contact with the pioneering computer that Vannevar Bush invented and which was developed under his close supervision. (Sam Caldwell, a professor of electrical engineering at MIT and a member of our war committee, had been a leading figure in the detailed design and construction.) And during the war it became evident that we were going to have electronic computers of unprecedented speed and logical flexibility, and with "memory" organs wherein vast amounts of information could be stored, any item of which could be made available to the computer in a fraction of a second.

Prospects of this general sort were clearly on the cards at the end of World War II. And a few years after the war

—in July 1949, in fact, while on a short vacation—I began to put on paper ideas that had been accumulating over the previous two or three years. What were we really going to do in our culture with this incredibly powerful new tool, the electronic computer?

In addition to all the obvious applications, two possibilities occurred to me; and I devoted time to each. The first of these concerned the relation of the computer to mathematics.

Classical mathematics appears to be implicitly and perhaps unconsciously based on the assumption that real quantities change continuously. This in turn stems from the idea that terrestrial material is itself ultimately continuous in its structure—totally without "graininess" no matter how minutely examined—as if it were, at whatever scale of magnification, the way butter looks under the naked eye.

And yet we know that this is not so. We know that matter (and also its alternative form, energy) is composed of discrete units. Discontinuity, not smooth continuity, is the ultimate and true nature of things.

Computation in a digital computer can be made as accurate as one wishes by utilizing a sufficient number of significant figures. But the calculation retains, in the last figure, a residual "graininess," in that that figure cannot change by less than one unit.

In these great computing engines we thus have a way of dealing with the quantitative aspects of nature which corresponds to nature's own structure. Continuity is an artifact: it is the spurious smoothness that results from lack of sufficiently fine and precise focus. When the German mathematician Leopold Kronecker (1823–1881) stated a century ago that "God made the integers. All else is the work of man," he actually had in mind a different and confused thing, but there has turned out to be a basic truth in his dictum.

Influenced by considerations of this sort, I believed that the computer might have a truly profound effect on the whole structure of mathematics, demanding a revised foundation which from the outset recognized discontinuity and discreteness as natural and necessary aspects of quantification.

Although there have been large developments to adapt mathematical procedures to suit the nature of the computer, the more revolutionary development of a discontinuity-based mathematics has not occurred, but I am still inclined to view this first idea which I had in 1949 as interesting but probably impractical.

The second idea concerning the impact of electronic computer developments was a strange one at the time, although it has since become familiar.

Early in 1947, having pondered the matter for nearly two years, I started to formulate some ideas about using computers to translate from one language to another. I first wrote this suggestion to the American mathematician Norbert Wiener (1894–1964), who was then teaching at MIT. I chose him because I knew him as a gifted linguist and brilliant logician. To my surprise and disappointment he was almost completely skeptical and discouraging about the idea. But I continued to turn the subject over in my mind, and in July 1949 I wrote a thirteen-page memorandum explaining why there was some real hope that translation could be done with computers.

Obviously, an efficient procedure for translating would be of great social service to the world, even if it did not produce elegant prose. It was by that time clear that computers could carry out any logically planned sequence of steps, however complex and extensive, at lightning speed. Memory organs would be available for storing vast data such as are found, for example, in Russian-English, Turkish-French, and other dictionaries.

There appeared to be two really serious difficulties: the ambiguity of meaning of many words ("fire" means to shoot, to set ablaze, to discharge from a job); and the apparently distinct and complicated ways in which the grammar (and more especially syntax) of various languages accommodate the expression of ideas. For both of these difficulties I had suggestions of ways in which they might be handled.[3] Being no student of linguistics, I was conscious that my ideas might be naïve or unworkable. But the possibilities so intrigued me that I had the memorandum mimeographed. I sent it to twenty or thirty persons—students of linguistics, logicians, and mathematicians. The first reaction was almost universally negative. A distinguished linguistic scholar later told me that after the initial reading he threw the paper in the waste basket; but waking in the night and thinking about it, he rescued the memo from the basket. Over the subsequent ten or fifteen years that scholar devoted a good part of his energy to the problem of machine translation.

There continues to be much work on this problem. Difficulties have arisen, as was to be expected. It would be absurd to hope for machine translations of literary works that would be acceptable from the point of view of style.

But there is a vast load of dull but necessary translation that need not be elegant; and by now it has been demonstrated that computers are capable of this.

The return to full duties at the Rockefeller Foundation after the war was a great joy to me—and for a special reason. All my life I have had the conviction that when a person takes on a new job, the curve of his effectiveness is low at first while he is breaking in (and for some unusual occupations this extends over a year or even longer), then should rise steadily for several years, but then tends to flatten out. In most cases, the horizontal asymptote is reached at a total span of about ten years. Only if circumstances change in some significant way is a person likely to continue to be freshly challenged by his job after that length of time.

Twice in my earlier life I had had about that span of years on a job—from 1921 to 1932, at the University of Wisconsin, and from 1932 until I started war work, at the Rockefeller Foundation. The five years of the war were such a complete change for me that I came back to my Rockefeller Foundation work as though it were a fresh opportunity.

In many ways it was. By 1945 the agricultural program had advanced enough so that it then occupied much of my time. It offered a fascinating new challenge. It was equally rewarding on three levels: the human importance of the problem of hunger with which it was concerned, the interest of the scientific problems with which I had to become familiar, and the managerial and political aspects of helping to work out the collaborative arrangements with a number of foreign governments.

The pattern of my travel was greatly altered. Before the war it had been largely confined to the United States and western Europe, with only an occasional trip elsewhere. After the war I continued to travel, somewhat less frequently, in Europe, but I also made regular visits to Mexico and South America, and extensive survey trips in Africa, India, Southeast Asia, and up to Japan.

The internal environment of the Rockefeller Foundation was equally stimulating. I served under four presidents, and I would gladly sponsor in any contest for outstanding individuals: Max Mason, Raymond B. Fosdick, Chester I. Barnard, and Dean Rusk. They were very unlike.

Max Mason was a scintillating genius, whose characteristics I have already set down.

Raymond Fosdick was, from the point of view of the operating officers, an ideal president. He was warm, friendly, full of stimulating questions. He depended heavily on the operating officers for technical judgments (which suited us perfectly), and he so completely had the confidence of the Board of Trustees that he could always smooth out our problems with them. All of us on the staff not only fully respected and trusted him, we had a deep affection for him.

Chester Barnard was president for only four years. He came—ostensibly at least—from industry, for he had been the President of the Bell Telephone Company of New Jersey. During his undergraduate years at Harvard he supported himself with three activities: he tuned pianos, he ran a dance band, and he himself conducted a translation service which dealt with three languages. Chester Barnard was born to be a scholar, and his distinguished industrial record was something of an accident. He had a most unusual mind. He used to drop down to my office late in the day, often would sit there smoking silently for some time, and then would come out with wholly unexpected remarks: "I am worried: everything is going too smoothly." Or "What is the relation between the half-life and the average life of a radioactive substance?"

At first we were all a little frightened by him. Promptly after his arrival I wrote him an office memo telling him that I had been in the habit of working at my home on Wednesdays, but that I would of course be in the office every day if he preferred that. He called me in, sat me in front of his desk, pointed to my memo and, looking rather grim, said, "I don't know if I approve of that!" Then before I could get my breath, he grinned and added, "Why don't you come in to the office on Wednesdays, and stay home and read and think all the other days?"

Shortly after that I wrote him another memo, criticizing something he had done. Again he called me in and sat me squarely facing him, again he looked pretty grim and said, "Don't ever do that again!" And then again he grinned and explained that he referred only to my having *written* the criticism. Circulating interoffice memos of that sort could, he thought, start incorrect and unfortunate rumors among the clerical staff. Next time, he told me, I ought to come in to his office, look him in the eye, and say, "Chester, you goddam fool, why did you . . ." From then on we were relaxed friends.

Chester Barnard thoroughly enjoyed the give-and-take with all the other officers. He almost always lunched at the big common table with a group of a dozen or more, and the conversation was totally unpredictable, but serious and rewarding.

One day at lunch he asked me if I had read, in the *Bell System Technical Journal,* an article by Claude E. Shannon on a mathematical theory of communication. I had. Did I understand the article? Not realizing the risk I was running, I answered yes. Could these ideas be explained in less formidably mathematical terms? Again, yes. "All right," he said, "do so."

This was the origin of the effort that led to the publication of a small book[4] that, surprisingly enough, after several seasons in hard covers is even now, eighteen years later, selling steadily as a paperback, advertised as a "classic"!

When Dean Rusk was made president no officer was surprised, for we had seen him in action for two years on the Board of Trustees and had surmised that this short period on the board was a planned preparation for his advancement. We had great respect for his mind and character; we all recognized the breadth and depth of his social commitment, and we liked him as a working colleague and friend.

It was inevitable that the variety of new contacts made during the war, and the activities that were war-related, would not cease abruptly in 1945. Some of these tied in with my Rockefeller Foundation activities—for example the continuing problem of relocation of deposed scholars, and the wide interest of many persons in developing our national strength in applied mathematics. The experience of the war had demonstrated the practical national, as well as the personal intellectual, value of work in this field, and had shown what history had in fact proved over the centuries— that mathematics, including its most "pure" and abstract portions, is healthiest and strongest during invigorating contact with a wide range of problems in the real world of experience.

For a few years after the war there were plans at several important locations for substantial, if not major, development of applied mathematics. It is distressing to have to record that in general these brave starts were not sustained. There are, fortunately, present indications of useful reintegration of all aspects of mathematics at several universities —Brown and Rochester, to mention only two important examples. And since the war there has been one truly significant development, at New York University.

Richard Courant, who had been the head of the world-renowned Institute of Mathematics at Göttingen, came to the United States early in the Hitler period. He became an American citizen in 1940; and when the Applied Mathematics Panel was formed in 1943 we chose Richard as a major member of the central directing and planning group. I had known him well before that, and as I worked with him during the war years, my admiration and affection grew. After the war it was inevitable that we thought and schemed together a great deal concerning ways to strengthen mathematics in the United States. With his scholarly leadership and organizing ability and energy, he gradually built up the advanced program in mathematics at New York University until it was clear that once again he was to be the director of a major world center.

Richard Courant is now, as a formal matter, retired; and so am I. But our many years of close association are permanently exemplified in the Courant Institute of New York University which is located in a beautiful new thirteen-story building named Warren Weaver Hall.

There were other activities that grew naturally out of the war experience. The accomplishments of Bush's OSRD had demonstrated to the armed services that they must continue to keep in close and productive relationship with research. The Navy was particularly alert to this problem, and especially skillful about developing its role. I was privileged to have some association with these military efforts, serving as Chairman of the Naval Research Advisory Committee and as a member of the War Department Research Advisory Panel (both during 1946–1947), and as Chairman of the Basic Research Group of the Research and Development Board of the War Department during 1952–1953.

Also in the service of the government, and obviously also related to the support of research, but differing in many other ways, was a period of service on the Board of the National Science Foundation. I would have to confess that I attended my first meetings of this board (which in effect bears just about the same relationship to the National Science Foundation that a board of trustees does to a philanthropic foundation) with some doubts, and perhaps even with some apprehensions, that I would find the Board of the National Science Foundation somewhat less admirable than the board of trustees of the Rockefeller Foundation. I was, to be sure, contrasting, in my doubts, a relatively new and inexperienced board with one which I had long considered the best possible. And it was difficult to avoid assuming that there would enter into the considerations of the National Science Board some elements of regional ambition, of political influence, or of institutional loyalty. And in the choice of the membership of this board, certain considerations undoubtedly entered which related to the balancing of geographical representation, and even some consideration of religion and race.

I found that my doubts were unjustified. I never listened to elements of debate in that board that the country as a whole could not have been proud of.

A quite differently oriented set of interests and activities developed at about this time, related not to the war but, at least initially, to my biological-medical contacts and experience within the Rockefeller Foundation. In 1951, Dr. Cornelius P. Rhoads, then the Director of the Sloan-Kettering Institute for Cancer Research, who had been both a personal and a professional friend of mine for years, asked me to be a member of his Board of Scientific Consultants. He thought that their program was making effective use of the techniques of chemistry, but he suspected that they were not exploiting the resources of physics as actively as they should. Because he thought of me primarily as a physicist, he thought I might be helpful.

I doubted that I could contribute, but I was certainly glad to try.

This began an association that grew and ramified over a sixteen-year period but ended in the spring of 1967 when I resigned from all but one of the appointments I held in the various parts of the Sloan-Kettering Memorial Cancer Center. My one remaining tie there is the chairmanship of a committee on bio-mathematics being developed jointly by Sloan-Kettering and Cornell Medical College.

These contacts, at that impressive medical crossroads at the four corners of Sixty-eighth Street and York Avenue in New York (do not forget that the Rockefeller University occupies one of these corners), have given me deep satisfaction. "The cancer problem" (which is of course a large array of interrelated problems) involves on the one hand scientific issues of real interest and general significance, and on the other hand it is a problem of the greatest human concern.

Growing out of contacts arising partly in the Rockefeller Foundation and partly at Sloan-Kettering, I became involved in three other health-related activities. During all its early years I was on the board of the Health Research Council of the City of New York—a unique organization most easily described as a biological-medical research foundation, supported out of New York City's own funds, and making grants to groups and individuals located in New York City. I was also on the board of (and later president of) the Public Health Research Institute of the City of New York, another unusual civic enterprise getting basic support from the regular budget of the City of New York, but also being substantially aided by research grants from Washington, and doing very fundamental research in areas related to metropolitan health problems.

Toward the end of my period of service in the Rockefeller Foundation I became interested in the Academy of Religion and Mental Health, which has by now developed into a major instrument for providing opportunities for collaboration between religious groups and those in the medical, social, and behavioral sciences. It is multiprofessional and multifaith. It has wide membership, sponsors an important journal, has held many successful conferences and symposia, conducts a research program, and holds approximately 500 branch meetings yearly. I served on the board of trustees of the academy for some time, and was deeply committed to its purposes. When a period of ill health forced me to be less active, I was made honorary vice president.

Still another area of activity that developed after the war was my involvement with the American Association for the Advancement of Science. This vast organization, with the largest membership of any general scientific society in the world, embraces all fields of pure and applied science. In the earlier days each branch of science conducted intensive sessions at which its own specialized research reports were given, and there was also some mild attempt to organize interdisciplinary sessions of general interest. Then the meetings got so large that they almost collapsed under their own weight. One group after another, first the chemists, then the physicists, the mathematicians, the biologists found it necessary to hold other and separate meetings. Attendance fell and the function of serving as a communication center between the various branches of science became less effective.

Elected first to the governing board of the AAAS, I participated in many discussions of ways to improve our annual meetings. Learning that the second of the two original charter purposes of the organization was to serve as a means of communication between science and the general public, I began to campaign for a rededication of the activities of the association. This gradually developed into a plan to hold a two-day conference at Arden House to examine our purposes, our plans, and our procedures. The report of this conference won enough interest and acceptance so that—having talked myself into a job, as so often happens—I was elected president of the AAAS for 1952. It is not easy to pin down this date, for the AAAS has, at any one moment, a president-elect, an active president, and a retiring president. It is a little like a major-league baseball game with one at bat, one on deck, and one in the hole. So this involved three more years of active participation in AAAS affairs. I have no notion that either my needling or my speeches had any permanent effect, but I did do something real and lasting when I helped to recruit Dael Wolfle as a new chief administrative officer of the AAAS. Under his leadership a worthy physical home for the AAAS was acquired, the membership has greatly increased, the weekly journal *Science* has vastly improved, and in these and other ways the association has prospered.

Over the fourteen-year period covered by this chapter my duties at the Rockefeller Foundation evolved and shifted substantially. The first few of these years involved considerable attention to cleaning up and tapering off interests that arose during the war. This was also a period of heavy concentration on the development of the agricultural program. After having been made the vice-president responsible for all the foundation's activities in the agricultural, natural, and medical sciences, it was necessary to turn over the detailed administration in these branches to able and experienced senior officers of these specialities. This in turn meant that I spent more and more office and travel time on general aspects of the foundation's work.

In 1959, at the statutory age of sixty-five and with over

a quarter of a century in the employ of the Rockefeller Foundation, I was retired in accordance with the rules of the organization.

"Retirement" can be a traumatic experience for those whose occupational interests have not included elements that can be carried forward into later years, and whose formal occupation has been so totally absorbing as to have excluded the development of other interests. I faced neither of these difficulties. My years at the Rockefeller Foundation were deeply satisfying to me. I loved my work. Every morning on the commuting train I would go over, with pleasurable anticipation, what was scheduled for that day. I hugely enjoyed my colleagues and the rich variety of interesting persons and problems.

But I believe in change and I have always enjoyed change. So in spite of the enthusiastic pleasure and satisfaction I had had throughout my years in the Rockefeller Foundation, I was not sad about leaving that behind. There were so many other things to do!

8. "Retirement"

My association with Alfred P. Sloan, Jr., began in 1954 when I was elected to the board of trustees of the Sloan-Kettering Institute for Cancer Research and then, soon after, made the chairman of that organization's Committee on Scientific Policy. All major questions concerning the scientific program of the institute (and later, of the center as a whole) were given detailed study by that committee, and its recommendations were then passed on to the board of trustees for formal action. The report of the chairman often involved an explanation of current or contemplated scientific activities in terms understandable to a board that included a majority of nonscientists. Because of Sloan's difficulties in hearing, I usually sat next to him and did my utmost to speak plainly and clearly.

I think he appreciated this, and my previous experience in interpreting scientific matters to a lay board thus, under these special circumstances, brought Mr. Sloan and me into a relationship which developed rapidly over the next two or three years.

Nearly two years before I was due to be retired at the Rockefeller Foundation, Sloan came to my office one day with a surprising proposal. Would I join the staff of the Sloan Foundation?

I felt greatly honored by the suggestion, but the situation was clear and I answered him at once. I was totally dedicated to my job at the Rockefeller Foundation. I could not conceive of leaving it until my time had run out.

Sloan replied equally promptly: "Good for you, Warren. If any one had ever asked me to leave General Motors I would have told them to go to hell." He then went on, "So let's talk about shifting when you retire." For the Sloan Foundation, as he explained with a chuckle, did not have a formal retirement age. Sloan was himself, at that time, past eighty.

A few days later I explained to Sloan that I had serious doubts about joining his staff, even on a part-time basis. My wife and I had by then built a permanent home in the country, just outside New Milford, Connecticut. We had looked forward to a life there that would involve a lot of gardening, which we both loved. My work in the Rockefeller Foundation had required me to be away from home a great deal, and I wanted to even up the account. I had, moreover, a host of personal projects to which I wanted to devote time.

Sloan swept away every reservation or difficulty with a generous countersuggestion. I was, in short, to work where I pleased, when I pleased, on what I pleased, only provided that I was prepared to interest myself in the problems of his foundation, to continue my activities at Sloan-Kettering, and to consult with him from time to time when mutually convenient. This sounded too good to be true, but Sloan meant precisely what he said. In every detail of our relationship he was extraordinarily thoughtful, always solicitous to protect my freedom of action, generous, and kind. Fantastic as it sounds, when he wanted to see me he did not ask that I come to him—he came to my office.

My candid relationship with him depended heavily on the fact that I had already run my main course. I had no long future ahead of me that could be seriously affected by my time at the Sloan Foundation. Sloan realized that I had nothing special at stake, to win or lose; and that I would therefore call the shots to him exactly as I saw them. He liked that.

As I think about him, a whole set of paradoxical opposites come to mind. He had—and after all, for good reason —a robust confidence in his own judgments; but with a few exceptions it was not a stubborn confidence. He was greatly concerned to get competent advice, and while he did not always follow it, he always weighed it.

One day he came, briskly as always, into my office and asked, "Do you think it too parochial [surprisingly, that was the word he used] of the Sloan Foundation to make grants only within the United States?" I told him that I thought we ought to make an occasional exceptional grant elsewhere. "Well—exceptional. That's just the point. We recently turned down a request from an engineering school in the Belgian Congo. We did right, didn't we?"

"No, I think that was a mistake."

"But Warren, no one here really *knew* anything about that school."

"Mr. Sloan, excuse me, but *I* know something about that school. I have visited it twice. I have real respect for its head, who has a doctor's degree from Princeton. And let me ask you three questions. First, do you think that the continent of Africa is going to emerge into the modern world during the next quarter century?"

"Well, of course.'

"Second, do you think Africa can take its place in the modern world if its own people have no competence in engineering?'

"Of course not."

"Third, can you name for me two places in black Africa where a native African can get really good training in engineering? And I will answer that one, for there is at present only one such place—the place we have decided against."

Sloan hesitated only a moment before saying, "When you make a mistake, there's only one sensible thing to do." He walked out, and promptly a notice was sent to the institution in question that the Sloan Foundation had granted them $50,000 for technical and scientific equipment. This, mind you, occurred when Sloan was about eighty-five.

He was capable of being pretty rough, in his language and in his judgments; but he was also a very gentle, thoughtful, and courteous man. For example, I almost never had a talk with him that did not include the remark, "And how is Mrs. Weaver? Please give her my regards."

One of the paradoxes that particularly baffled me was Sloan's great respect for basic research and for the imaginative and pioneering mind, as contrasted with his often really violent condemnation of "professors" and of the "academic mind." I put these terms into quotes; he had private definitions! At various times, I pointed out to him as vigorously as I could that the word "academic" admittedly had in certain circles the weak connotation of "impractical, theoretical, not expected to produce an immediate result," but also had the strong connotation, going back at least as far as Plato's Academy, of "scholarly, showing full and detailed knowledge of the subject" (both sets of terms being taken from Webster). Sloan was convinced that "professors" lacked incentive, and that their profession suffered from having no tangible way in which performance could be measured—no profit-and-loss statement at the end of the year. Indeed, he was convinced that no "professor" ever *really worked hard*. And since certain foundations were staffed largely with ex-professors, he also had a low opinion of the energy and courage of those foundations. He once remarked to me that foundations hardly needed any retirement regulations, because their officers "might rust out, but would never wear out."

He and I argued this matter of the academic mind and attitude on many occasions. I insisted that I had been *driven*, within the small world of my competence and experience, just as relentlessly as he had been in the admittedly vaster world in which he operated. I told him that professors did not need, did not want, and never could respect the special incentive of "bonuses" and other such "profit-sharing" devices. But I truthfully think that he never really believed this.

One day, after he had let loose a particularly vigorous blast against the academic mind, I asked him how he could hold such views yet still give such great support, personally and through his foundation, to the academic institution known as the Massachusetts Institute of Technology. The reply (which might have dismayed the Boston authorities) was, "MIT is *not* an academic institution! It is a technological institute!"

Sloan's presence was a continuous stimulation to the officers of his foundation. He would storm in and let loose a volley against "complacent mediocrity" and for "dynamic imagination." He had a deep-seated distrust—really a disdain—of small grants. These he considered "handouts." Importance tended to be measured by size, and size tended to be measured by the amount of money voted.

It is also indubitably the case that Sloan was not greatly interested in the ideas that came into the foundation from universities—he was interested in the ideas that were generated within his own organization. And this remark needs two emphatic additions: in most instances these ideas came from Sloan himself, and in practically all instances they were first-rate.

I have here been referring to "his foundation" and there is no doubt that the possessive pronoun is correct. But Sloan's domination did *not* center in the fact that he had earned and contributed the money; it centered in the fact that he had the brains and the imagination. He ceaselessly and probingly sought new ways to advance the two causes most important to him: basic research and an understanding of the economics of the free-enterprise system. He exerted leadership simply because he had the attributes of a leader.

He had so many ideas that they could not all be ten-strikes. One morning he came in and told me of a plan that had occurred to him. It seemed to me just impossible, but I promised to think about it and write him my conclusions. I did so, and two days later he merely stuck his head in my door, grinned, and said, "Forget it—it was terrible!"

His record is such that it would not be altered by any minor comment that I could make; but I am bound to say that my association with him—a surprisingly intimate one—

was continuously stimulating and rewarding, and led to a feeling of affection and deepest respect. He was a truly great man.

My relationship with the Sloan Foundation was quite different from that which I had earlier had with the Rockefeller Foundation. The procedures in the Sloan Foundation when I joined it were, for example, far different from those I had been used to. There were at that time no staff meetings and no general staff discussions; each officer worked directly with Sloan. At trustee meetings Sloan, as the presiding officer, gave extraordinarily clear and complete reports of all financial aspects of the foundation's business, and he himself described—with no notes, in a meticulously accurate way and often with a touch here and there of penetrating humor—the proposals on which the board was to act. The meetings were never long. Sloan always commenced by thanking the trustees for their interest and their presence; and when the business had been briskly concluded—extended discussion was of course handicapped by his deafness—the meetings were promptly terminated.

The actions themselves—at least speaking of areas within which I had had training and experience—seemed to me first-rate and unquestionably in the public interest. But the extent to which all this depended upon the special genius of a man approaching ninety seemed to me worrisome.

Thus a great deal of my effort, especially over the first two or three years, was devoted to getting Mr. Sloan to recognize that it was essential that some less personalized organization be planned and staffed. I told him bluntly that as things then were, his knowledge, his insights, his experience, his vision, and his ideals would end abruptly on that inevitable morning when he failed to show up. (He had no morbid sensitivity whatsoever about death, and often said, half-wryly and half in fun, that he was living on borrowed time.) I suppose I was the only one around the office in a position to urge him to resign as president and bring in someone who could work with him and could thus be able to carry on the fine tradition he had established. After I had brought this up several times he invited me to his apartment for dinner one evening—the only time I was ever there—and in a long talk he said that he had decided to make the move.

Although exceedingly generous about many things, and not averse to spending money—a dinner given to some group was always at the Waldorf, with everything just right —he took a very close look at the administrative budget of the Sloan Foundation itself. He did this, I have reason to know, for wholly unselfish and fine motives: he told me once he wanted *every dollar possible* to go in grants. I countered with the sort of argument I knew would appeal to him: that if $10,000 spent in the office would improve by one per cent the efficiency with which $10 million of grants were distributed, then was not this a bargain? When I came in, there was a very small staff, no office manager, the secretary-treasurer had to order routine office supplies, the assistant treasurer was supposed to keep an eye on the secretaries and clerical persons, and if you wanted a ticket bought or a book wrapped up for mailing you had your secretary do it, or did it yourself. This was, actually, not nearly as bad as it sounds. The great national genius on creating and managing a huge organization wanted to keep this operation simple; and he succeeded in this, as he did in practically everything else.

What troubled me more was the tradition of the front desk that a foundation officer was tending to business when he was in the office; but if he was out wandering around universities and elsewhere, gathering ideas and listening to wants and needs, this was viewed somewhat skeptically. Sloan was used to generating ideas and plans—he was superb at it—and I think it fair to say that if someone came to him with a fully developed scheme, one which did not require his collaboration except in terms of money, that person might be a very game fish but he was certainly swimming upstream.

Well before Sloan's death on February 17, 1966, at the age of nearly ninety-one, the organization and procedures of the Sloan Foundation had been materially changed. Significant additions had been made to both the professional and the service staff. Most important of all, Everett Case, previously the president of Colgate University, became the new president of the Sloan Foundation. With great skill he served internally as the leader of the staff of officers, he worked excellently with and for Sloan, and with marked success he collaborated with the board of trustees. Saddened as we all were by Sloan's death, it was a great satisfaction to us that his foundation could sustain this loss and rededicate itself to the ideals he had established.

After five years as a vice-president of the Sloan Foundation I felt that I had doubtless made what minor contribution I could, and I asked to have the commitments between myself and the foundation mutually reduced. Accordingly in 1964 I was shifted from the vice-presidency and made consultant for scientific affairs. At about the same time retirement rules were adopted, so that presently I no longer was a trustee. These moves, and a new schedule of coming into New York about twice a month, gave me still more freedom for other interests.

One of these was a growing involvement in the Salk Institute for Biological Studies. I first met Jonas Salk in April 1960, when he came into my office and told me something of the plans for the new research institute of which he was to be the director. On this initial meeting I questioned him probingly on certain aspects of his plans, and when he left I had a hunch that I was unlikely to see him again. But soon he was back, expressing his appreciation for the frankness of our first talk, and wanting to go on with the discussion.

Before long I became really captivated both by Jonas himself and by the idea of the institute. It was to be small and flexible. It was to have no "departments" in the classical sense of university structure. It was to deal with the biological sciences on their most modern and growing frontiers. It might eventually develop other educational activities, but for the near future at least its temporary personnel would chiefly be postdoctoral persons. Its regular staff would consist of a relatively small number of outstanding individuals, each of whom would develop a program centered around his own interests. These full-time "fellows" were to be supplemented by a roughly equal number of "nonresident fellows," each of whom would spend a period every year at the institute. The initial strength was to be in molecular biology, virology, immunology, and similar interrelated disciplines, with probable expansion into some areas of behavioral biology

All this sounds good; but why did I think the Salk Institute promised to be something so special? For one thing, several full-time and nonresident fellows were already chosen, and the level of these appointments was extraordinarily high. The group of nonresident fellows included Francis Crick from Cambridge, England, and Jacques Monod of the Pasteur Institute in Paris—two world leaders, both of whom were presently to receive Nobel Prizes. In general, the nonresident fellows were to establish a mode of communication between the Salk Institute and a number of important universities and institutes spread over the United States and elsewhere. The location at La Jolla was superb, and impressive and beautiful laboratories were already designed by a distinguished architect. The National Foundation, doubtless at least in part to express their great admiration of and continuing confidence in the man who had developed a successful polio vaccine under their auspices,* had pledged a substantial amount of money toward the initial capital costs and also toward yearly expenses.

This, however, was by no means all. It was an explicit part of the basic plan that the most rigorously experimental and analytical aspects of biology be developed at this new institute in close and continuing association with humanistic studies which, at artistic, philosophical, and moral levels would seek to interpret the scientific advances in terms of man's ideals and needs, and which, by the mere close presence of such concerns, would influence the trend of the scientific studies along lines that would seek to heighten man's potentialities and help him to lead a fuller and richer life.

*More precisely, under the auspices of the National Foundation for Infantile Paralysis, which in 1958 was renamed the National Foundation.

As a main expression of this unusual—and to me extremely promising and tempting concept—it had been arranged that one of the full-time resident fellows would be Jacob Bronowski, the almost incredible British mathematician, logician, philosopher, essayist, dramatist, and poet, the author of a number of superb books which interpret to a general audience the nature of science and its relation to other creative enterprises, the practical organizer of a huge postwar research program under the Coal Board in England, and an outstanding authority on the poet William Blake. I am sure that I have left out some of Bruno's qualifications, but perhaps my point has been made. There was no aspect of the most detailed and technical work of the institute that he could not understand, illuminate, interpret, and enrich.

It is pretty embarrassing to offer a full symphonic orchestra, and then a solo on the piccolo. But I must in honesty mention that I could not help being pleased and moved that I was offered a position as a nonresident fellow, the range (though obviously neither the intensity nor the competence) of my interests being a cut-down version of those of Bronowski.

Thus to my surprise, I found myself becoming more and more involved. Since it was wholly consistent with the unorthodox policies of the institute that a person be located on both sides of almost any fence, I was also made a trustee and for a few early years served as the chairman of the board. For three winters I spent a period at the institute. Then health difficulties developed, but as I write this, we plan to go back to La Jolla.

The institute has had some birth pains, as I suppose

is natural. It badly needs broader and larger support. In long retrospect, it is now easy to see that certain mistakes were made at the outset. But the plan, I am convinced, is a sound and even noble one. There are at present essentially no difficulties that money would not solve; and I simply cannot believe that this handicap will long persist. I have been privileged to observe the birth of two noteworthy institutions—the California Institute of Technology and the Salk Institute. In both instances the concept was a great one; and I am confident that the second of the two, although destined for a future quite unlike that of the former, will add another great star to the constellation of scientific organizations of our country.

The freedom of the later years provided time for another project which I had been considering for a long time. My experience in the Rockefeller and Sloan foundations, along with overlapping experience in a number of other fund-granting agencies (the General Education Board, the National Science Foundation, the Research Corporation, the council of the National Cancer Institute, the Health Research Council of New York City, the Council on Library Resources), had led me to three conclusions. First, the great private philanthropic foundations serve our society in a most beneficial and significant way. Second, they are not only little understood—they are often badly misunderstood. Third, any social instrument will be allowed to continue only if, in the long run, it is understood and approved by people in general.

In the earlier days of the Rockefeller Foundation the

public relations policy was one of overmodest reticence. Do good things, say nothing about them, and eventually the world will find you out and honor you.

This better-mousetrap policy, however, overlooked several important points. As the number of philanthropic foundations greatly increased (there are today more than 6,000 with substantial assets), it was unfortunately true that some were used for selfish and improper purposes. In the days of high personal and corporation taxes, any activity that is untaxed comes under special and sometimes prejudiced scrutiny. And there are always those politicians or the muckraking type of writers who profit from the exaggerated exposure of exceedingly rare errors in a vast record of good deeds.

It therefore seemed important to me to make available the story of the special kind of philanthropy that is practiced by the major and mature foundations in America. Discussion with foundation officials indicated their agreement with this idea. Thus, with initial encouragement from the Rockefeller Foundation, with substantial support to the project from the Sloan Foundation, and under the sponsorship of the American Academy of Arts and Sciences, I undertook the job of preparing a book. I worked on this manuscript for about four years, and it was published in 1967.[1]

Opinions as to the degree of foundation success in various fields would inevitably be suspect when stated by one who had been a philanthropoid for thirty-five years. Accordingly I planned the book to consist of two parts. The first part, dealing primarily with "History, Structure, and Management," I wrote myself. The second part, dealing with "Record," consists of eighteen rather short chapters, each of which was written by a world authority in some field (chemistry, medicine, education, law, the visual arts, international affairs, economics, and others). Each author stated, on the basis of his own direct professional experience, the values and also the limitations of the aid his particular field of interest had received from philanthropic foundations.

When the philanthropy book was well along, I became involved in gathering and updating a series of papers I had previously written on a wide variety of topics.[2]

Finally I was invited to write the present work, so that for a time I was in the unexpected position of having three books in preparation at once.

9. Science Then and Now

Suppose that in some magic way an unborn individual could be told that he is going to live for about three fourths of a century. In order to have the richest possible experience, when would he like to have that period begin? The answer would of course depend on the nature and range of the interests of the person in question. Some would, understandably, choose the age of Pericles. Some surely would choose the Elizabethan age. If the person is to be chiefly interested in science, then I think he might sensibly choose my own period, beginning with 1894. Benjamin Franklin, looking ahead with remarkable vision in 1780, wrote to the English clergyman and chemist Joseph Priestley (1733–1804), "the rapid progress science now makes occasions my regretting sometimes that I was born too soon." I have no similar regret. I had the good luck to be born at the right time.

Why do I think I was born at the right time? For a person whose interests and activities have been primarily in science, the answer is bound to be, at least in part, because of the exciting and majestic developments in science during my lifetime.

But these scientific developments do not constitute the complete answer to the question just posed. Important and fascinating as science is, there are numerous other concerns of men that are essential to a good life. At the beginning of this book, I mentioned that the front page of the issue of *The New York Times* on the day of my birth contained essentially no national news, and no international news whatsoever. I was born into what, in retrospect, seems a somnolent world, whose leaders acted like sleepwalkers. The savage wars, the social tumult, the frenzied unrest of some of the years since I was born have been in many ways frightfully disturbing. But all this is a sign of life and vigor, of sensitivity, of concern for the human condition, and it is, I believe, a sign pointing toward ultimate progress. Thus in addition to being thankful for living through some of the proudest days of science, I am also thankful for living at an exciting time of political and social movement. Dark as the prospect has often seemed, I have faith that the world has, during this period, been groping toward the light, and I appreciate having been able to sense and observe all this movement.

The more serious and significant aspects of the progress of science during my lifetime could, of course, only be described in technical terms. To the trained scientist, the significant advances are likely to be improvements in complicated and abstract basic theories. These improvements give the theories greater precision, broader application, and increased esthetic grandeur. These improvements are often too technical and too abstract to seem impressive to the nonscientist. But it is just these deep and abstract improvements in basic theories which presently give scientists a more effective control over natural forces, and which thus lead to the technological improvements that touch and serve everyone.

Thus it is brought about that people in general are likely to be aware of scientific progress as evidenced by its by-products, rather than aware of the progress in the inner core of scientific thought. This is a great pity, for that inner core of scientific thought is one of the most beautiful and most impressive products of the imaginative human mind. As science education improves in all levels of our schools, and as competent public interpretation of science advances, our society should approach an improved state in which more and more of the marvelous inner structure of science can be appreciated by everyone. In the meantime, it remains embarrassingly true that the practical results of applied science are, for many persons, the basis upon which their estimates of science necessarily rest. So, regretfully, I accept the fact that an effective way of giving a generally understandable description of the way science progresses over a period is to cite the improvement, over that period, of the practical procedures or devices, aids to everyday living, made possible by scientific advance.

I will therefore start by reminding the reader of some technological changes which science has made possible during the past seventy-five years, these being changes that affect all of us.

I am confident, from having conducted a small private poll on the question, that when asked, "What has changed most over the past seventy-five years?" the answer is likely to be, "Transport and communication."

I will presently cite some arithmetical facts, but all of the contrast between transport in 1894 and transport now is not to be captured in numbers. When I was a small boy my maternal grandparents lived in a tiny village about fifty miles from our home; and once or twice each year, my father would decide to risk driving our automobile that distance. This journey was not undertaken lightly. In preparation, my father would clean and reset the spark plugs, would check on the supply of patches and cement for mending an inner tube, and would carefully check up on the carbide system which supplied the headlights with gas, should darkness overtake us. The fifty-mile journey, with time out for a picnic lunch and for roadside repairs, sometimes took the better part of a day. But what is a day's journey now? The last time my wife and I came home from Europe, we had breakfast in Paris and dinner in our own house in Connecticut.

All the advantage in transport, however, is not to be credited to today. We can now, to be sure, travel much faster than we used to. But we have lost something in convenience, and in comfort, and in style. One of the thrills of my youth was a trip on a train. A meal in a dining car, at the turn of the century, was a glamorous, elegant, and altogether pleasant affair. To be sure, one now has gourmet meals at an altitude of over 30,000 feet, and an airline is apologetic if it does not broil your steak in flight, and to order. But the valley of western Connecticut where I live now has passenger train service only on weekends; and the occasional train is pretty shabby-looking.

The speed of modern transport is indeed impressive, especially to one who recalls the flights at Kitty Hawk in 1903. But, surprisingly, the 600 miles per hour of the present-day commercial jet aircraft is only about 150 times as fast as the speed of a brisk walk. The orbital speed of our astronauts, circling the globe in about ninety minutes at an altitude of a hundred miles, is only slightly more than 4,000 times as fast as the speed of walking. If one thinks of instances of the numerical gain achieved by technology since 1894, the case of transport speed is a mild instance.

A modern electronic computer, which in one minute can carry out as much arithmetic computation as a skilled human computer can achieve in a lifetime, furnishes an instance of speed-up by a factor of almost forty million. If there had occurred an equal speed-up in transport, a flight today from New York to London would take less than one thousandth of a second! An instance of an increase that is even greater than the speed-up in computing is furnished by the fact that an atom of coal can furnish two or three electron volts of energy, whereas an atom of uranium 235 yields in fission 200 million electron volts.

The cited numerical increases in speed of transport, in speed of computing, in available energy are impressive. In fact, they are more significant than is indicated by the numerical factors. For when technology increases the speed of any process or the amount of any quantity—for instance, a quantity of available energy—by, say, 10 or 20 per cent, this quantitative change can be useful and important. But when a quantity is increased by a very large factor—say, a billion —then a surprising thing often happens. Indeed, a large enough change in *quantity* often results in a change in *quality*. For example, if through developments in nuclear physics man has available to his purposes billions of times as much energy as he had before, it does not suffice merely to say that he has a lot more energy. He has, in fact, something quite other than what he had before. He now has so much energy that he can realistically think of attacking problems that were previously totally insuperable. For example, he might now think of desalting enough sea water to make deserts bloom; or of changing climate by melting the polar ice caps or by altering ocean currents.

Speed of computing is a good technological illustration of the magic shift from quantity to quality. When the speed of computation is stepped up by a factor of 10^7, then it is no longer sufficient to say "This new device is notably more rapid than its predecessors." For that much gain in speed proves to be more than just gain in speed. The new device not only does all previous computing tasks much faster; it also opens up previously inaccessible possibilities.

Suppose, for instance, that astronomers have an excellent and complete theory for the motion of, say, the moon. But suppose that this theory is so complicated that the computation of the path of the moon over a period of a month requires perhaps two months. Then predictions of future positions cannot be computed out rapidly enough to be useful. You can't compute, so to speak, as fast as the moon moves, so you cannot usefully predict the moon's future positions. This, incidentally, is not a fanciful example but an actual one.

Another example is the computation of the aerodynamic and thermodynamic equations which describe the motion of our atmosphere. These computations are so complex and extensive that long-range weather forecasting would be completely unthinkable if one were limited to the type of computing that was possible before the electronic computer. It would be wholly unfair to the new device merely to say that it does these computations faster than they could be done before. The gain that results from the new device is not just a quantitative gain, it is a qualitative gain. The modern electronic computer, in fact, makes possible a quantitative attack on many kinds of problems that previously were prohibitively complex. It is, indeed, almost impossible to imagine, in advance, the usefulness of such a device. In today's mail, as I write this, I find an invitation to attend a summer conference under impeccably competent and serious auspices, to be devoted to a consideration of "Computers and Religion." Who, twenty-five years ago (to say nothing of seventy-five years ago) would have taken seriously such a title!

To turn, now, to the record of the second most frequently cited item of contrast between the present day and the past, it is surely true that the last years have seen a spectacular advance in communication. As for the telephone, radio, and television, the improvement is in my case measured from zero, for in my childhood we had no telephone, and we did not dream of radio or television. All three modes of communication have, in fact, enormously improved in the last quarter century, not to mention the last three quarters. The present direct phone dialing across our continent and the quality of transmission are almost miracles of scientific ingenuity and engineering skill. And when, in the living room of a house in Connecticut, one can observe in color, via satellite, events as they are taking place in Europe, he should, at least once in a while, stop to contemplate the amount of scientific and engineering genius that has been applied to the design and construction of all the instrumentation involved, not forgetting the reliability of the unattended receiving and transmitting equipment in the satellite, nor the recently acquired skill which permits placing the satellite accurately in an orbit that leaves it in a position fixed relatively to the revolving earth. The sensitivity of the modern receiving equipment is well indicated by the fact that a dependable signal can be sent to the earth from equipment on the surface of the moon, using less than 10 watts of power. This is so small and weak a power source that it is unlikely that the reader has in his house an electric globe of as little as 10 watts. That is the size that is traditionally used in the back hall of an Italian *pensione,* but hardly anywhere else.

The great improvements in transport and communication touch all of us; but they do not affect our modern lives as frequently as do many other products of today's technology. To sense the ubiquity and the immediacy of the aids to the mechanics of living that serve us today and that were not available during my youth, just look about you in your house. Especially in the kitchen! The modern stove, the dishwasher, the refrigerator, the freezer, both of the latter containing examples of the pre-prepared foods carried by every supermarket—all of these are comparatively recent. The kitchen in my own home, and it is by no means extraordinary in its equipment, profits from the silent and ever available service of nearly a dozen electric motors. It seems a trivial and, in a sense, almost ridiculous item of testimony to the way technology now serves us to note, on one wall, an electric can opener! But that this device is a welcome aid in the modern home is evidenced by the fact that Macy's now carries twenty-two models of electric can openers.

Near the beginning of this book I spoke of the kitchen in the small house of my Grandmother Weaver. It did not have any cupboards or cabinets, for in those days everyone had a pantry. In addition to the wood-burning range the only other piece of equipment that I recall was a hand-operated, or better, an arm-operated water pump. It did, however, have one other very important piece of equipment, and that was a large and generously supplied cookie jar, always available to small boys.

Two modern devices in the kitchen and service end of the house have a special flavor for me, in terms of the contrast with my youth. One morning each week, in my earliest teens, I got up early so as to have time, before school, to turn the wringer for my mother, as she did the weekly wash. And on Saturday morning, I remember, as I glance at the vacuum cleaner in the closet, it was my regular duty to take the smaller rugs out to the back yard and beat the dust out of them.

I had another household task that serves to highlight the difference between then and now. In my present home, newspapers are saved for starting fires in our living-room fireplace. In the home of my youth they were saved for me to use them, crumpled up, to clean out the major accumulation of soot in the glass chimneys of our kerosene lamps. Now, one of our electric clocks turns on the lights in our living room at dusk, and turns them out after we have gone to bed.

Yes, science and technology now touch us every hour of every day, as they certainly did not in the 1890s. Chelsea House has just issued a facsimile reproduction of the 1897 Sears Roebuck catalogue. From this, a vivid and fascinating picture of the contrast, between 1897 and now, in household equipment and conveniences can be quickly gained. The section on household utensils contains many models of wood or coal stoves, galvanized washtubs, coal scuttles, and mop wringers, but not a single electrically operated device. For the entertainment of the family there were musical instruments, books, magic lanterns, and stereopticons with slides of Uncle Tom being sold and leaving his family, of Yellowstone Park, and of Bible scenes.

To move up several levels of significance from the trivial one of gadgetry, a major contrast between now and my earliest days is to be found in the progress—here very closely correlated with the advances of scientific knowledge in the biological and related sciences—in the prevention, control, and cure of diseases.

A person born in the United States in 1900 had a life expectancy of about forty-six years. At the present time, this figure has been increased, by medical science, to 66.8 for males and 73.7 for females. In 1900 the age-adjusted death rate, from all causes, was 1,778.5 per 100,000 population. Today this has been spectacularly reduced to 741.8. In the case of some of the dread childhood diseases of 1900, the gain to the present has been spectacular. For measles during the first four years of life, the death rate figure in 1900 was 87.6; today it is 0.4. The same figures for whooping cough have been reduced from 60.2 to 0.1. Diphtheria was a dangerous childhood disease in 1900, the death rate for children during their first four years being 271.0 per 100,000. The present figure is so near zero that it is seldom recorded.

The record of the last few decades in the almost complete conquering of the infectious diseases is a bright and important item in the health contrast between then and now. The very recent conquest of polio also deserves a glittering citation, and it is hard to suppress the optimistic conviction that we are now on the threshold of great gains with respect to heart disease and cancer.

These advances have required the most dedicated service of some of our most gifted scientists. The pace of this advance has been rapid in the more recent years. A great many of the important drugs carried by a drug store today were unknown and undreamed of even a quarter of a century ago. Imagine the bewilderment of my father if he could step out of his small drug store of 1894 into the prescription department of his modern successor.

I stated earlier my conviction that I was born at the right time. Indeed, I would claim that I picked almost precisely the right time. All of us today are conscious that we are living in the electronic age. In 1897, when I was only three years old, the British physicist Sir Joseph John Thomson (1856–1940), noting that cathode rays could be deflected by a magnetic field, discovered the electron and initiated our present era. When I was one year old, the German physicist Wilhelm Konrad Roentgen (1845–1925) discovered X rays, which were to prove indispensable to medicine and surgery as well as a fine tool for exploring the structure of matter. With these two central discoveries, there began what is surely the richest, the most exciting period the physical sciences have ever experienced.

In spite of the great advances during the seventy-four-year interval from 1894 to 1968 in biology, medicine, and other fields of science, I think the most striking and most profound change has occurred in physics. It would be incorrect to give the impression that the contrast arises because nineteenth-century physics was a slowly or weakly developing subject. Although the foundations had been laid earlier for the whole great field of dynamics, the nineteenth century saw the emergence of much of our modern large-scale knowledge of electricity, magnetism, and electrodynamics. Giving a good practical knowledge of the action of large-scale electrical forces, these developments made possible the industrial revolution which replaced steam power by electrical power, and which initiated, late in the century, the myriad uses of electric motors and the marvels of electric lighting, of telephony, and of wireless telegraphy.

Once the electron had been discovered, the attack on the secrets of atomic structure was dramatically rapid and successful. In 1913 there was published the first of a series of truly epoch-making papers on atomic structure by Niels Bohr. The first transmutation of one element into another —nitrogen to oxygen—was accomplished in 1919 by the British physicist Sir Ernest Rutherford (1871–1937).

The amazing minds of the ancient philosophers—and poets—speculated about the ultimate constitution of matter, but they had only imagination and analogy as tools. The opening-up of the atomic world, subsequently extended into the still smaller nuclear world, is one of the greatest of man's triumphs, and this exploration effectively began just before the turn of the century.

This, however, is only a small part of the story, for there have been two other developments in physics during my lifetime, even more original, more profound, and more far-reaching in their implications. These, of course, are relativity theory and quantum theory. The former was begun in Einstein's restricted theory of 1905, and magnificently extended in the general theory which appeared in 1916. The second was quantum theory, which originated as something startlingly new and indeed even bizarre, with ideas that the German physicist Max Planck (1858–1947) announced in 1900. Planck affirmed that energy was not a smoothly and continuously divisible entity, capable of existing in any amount, but rather that energy existed in discrete, indivisible bits. The validity of this powerful and strange new concept was confirmed by theoretical work on the photoelectric effect which Einstein published in 1905 and was later experimentally confirmed by Millikan.

Relativity and quantum theory opened up wholly new regions of physics, truly undreamed of when I was born; and each of these had tremendous philosophical consequences as well. The complete collapse of any idea of the absolute measurement of time, the blending of space and time into a four-dimensional complex, the destruction of the physical concept of continuity, the puzzling but inescapable fact that an electron is both a particle and a wave and the resulting concept of complementarity, the shattering of determinacy in the world of ultimate particles (explained in Chapter 10); the release of nuclear energy—these were scientific episodes of a majestically new power and sweep.

The advance of physics during my lifetime has involved the elaboration of theories which, with almost unbelievable precision, deal with an ever greater array of physical phenomena, not only at molecular and atomic dimensions, but also even at nuclear dimensions. In the advance of solid-state physics (the theories concerning the detailed behavior of the electric entities which form solid pieces of matter—for instance, pieces of metal or crystalline substances) one of the recent dramatic episodes has been the design and construction, even on regular commercial schedules, of solid-state microelectronic devices. These reduce entire electronic circuits, previously filling the whole interior of a good-sized radio, to such tiny dimensions that a square silicon chip less than one one hundredth of an inch thick and about one tenth of an inch on a side can, by a complicated and delicate manufacturing procedure, be made equivalent to 100 to 500 integrated circuits, each containing 10 to 20 transistors and, say, 50 resistors. These minuscule devices require, moreover, very little energy and generate very little heat. They are so rugged and dependable that they can be used in solid-fuel missiles. The matchbox radios that football fans take to the stadium so that they can also overhear other games have seemed to us marvels of compact skill. But the new micro-micro techniques can reduce the circuitry of a large section of an electronic computer to the volume dimensions of a thimble.

The record of physics, especially from about 1920 to today, is a dazzling one indeed, penetrating ever deeper and deeper into the behavior of matter, and furnishing dependable guides for the construction and use of ever more complicated devices.

As an intellectual tour de force, the world has probably never before seen anything like this. The complexity and precision of the theories demand and merit the greatest admiration.

Closely associated with the explosive growth of physics have been the developments in astronomy since 1894.

In 1894, astronomers were pretty sure that the Milky Way was a star system some 10,000 to 20,000 light-years in diameter, and there was no certainty that there was anything farther out. The distance determinations of that time depended upon parallax measurements, and these became ineffective at distances of about 100 light-years, so that larger figures were based on speculation only. Nowadays the boundaries extend to something like ten billion light-years, the extreme evidence being subject to uncertainties in the application of relativity theory to objects whose red shift is large.

In 1894 nuclear energy was unthought of, and astronomers believed that the sun derived its energy from gravitational attraction. On that basis, the age of the sun was then estimated to be something like fifteen million years, whereas today we believe the age of the sun to be about six billion years.

In addition to continuous and steady progress in all aspects of astronomical knowledge, there have emerged, especially over the last decade or so, a number of exciting new types of problems which now confront the astronomer. There have been located in the sky extremely powerful sources of radio energy, especially in the very short X-ray wave-length regions; these are often, if not usually, unassociated with any optically visual celestial object. The nature of these sources and their possible relation to the birth or death of stars present a whole array of puzzling and fascinating problems. Very recently, moreover, signals have been received from well-defined and angularly small regions of the sky, these signals being wholly extraordinary in that they are periodic in character, the intervals between successive signals being strangely precise. These have inevitably caused curiosity as to whether some advanced sentient forms of life may exist elsewhere and may be trying to communicate with us. All this is as yet wholly speculative in nature, but hints at how much astronomy still has to learn.

It is certainly incorrect to say that the twentieth century has seen the disappearance of chemistry as a discipline in its own right, but nevertheless a great deal of the most fundamental, and most of the purely theoretical, chemistry has now become indistinguishable from physics. Indeed, two of the men who have had the greatest influence on the development of chemistry in this century, the Dutch-American physical chemist Peter Pieter Debye (1884–1966) and Linus Pauling, have used techniques and ideas that came chiefly from physics; Debye, in fact, was often, if not usually, classified as a physicist.

Some of the most outstanding accomplishments of modern chemistry lie in the field of organic synthesis—the production by the chemist, often starting with materials which are totally inorganic in nature, of substances which imitate, and which often improve upon, those previously produced by nature. One thinks at once of all the artificial fibers that make possible wrinkleproof and stainproof cloth, of the plastics that have become such familiar servants of our everyday needs, of the synthetic rubber out of which, along with imbedded bands of nylon or other synthetic fabric, longer-wearing and safer tires can be made. A number of the most complicated natural products which are used by the physicians, such as quinine, morphine, and insulin, have by now been produced in the laboratory. The 1930s saw the synthesis of a number of the vitamins—a vitamin was defined by the German-American biochemist Rudolph

Schoenheimer (1898–1941) as "something that makes you sick if you don't eat it."* However, the syntheses of these biologically important substances, having from twenty to seventy atoms per molecule, were overshadowed by more complicated and difficult triumphs which principally began in the 1940s.

In many instances the chemist is now able to decide what properties his new material could most usefully have, and can then fabricate to these specifications, often outdoing nature. The magnitude and the practical economic importance of the work of the chemists are indicated by the fact that a recent study found that the chemical industry is directly responsible for $27 billion a year of our gross national product, and that this scientific technical industry provides the materials that are indispensable for other industries which account for $67 billion of our gross national product. The record of the creation of improved new synthetic fibers by chemistry is clearly not a closed story. A recent newspaper article reported that the Du Pont company had just displayed clothing made from a new silklike fiber on whose creation the company has spent more than $75 million over a twenty-year period. In luster, color clarity, dyeability, and draping characteristics the cloth woven from this new synthetic material is said to be equivalent to the most luxurious silk fabrics.

A large part of the spectacular advance of the biological sciences in the twentieth century has centered around the

* Knowledge of the deficiency diseases began with the diagnosis of beri-beri in 1897 by the Dutch bacteriologist Christiaan Eijkman (1858–1930).

rise in genetics which started in 1900. In fact, practically all the other great advances in biology either stem from that or are related to it.

The pioneer work of the Austrian biologist Gregor Mendel (1822–1884) in discovering the basic laws of inheritance was a nineteenth-century achievement, his important results having been published in an obscure journal in 1866. But it was not until 1900 that this work was rediscovered practically simultaneously by three botanists: the Dutch Hugo De Vries (1848–1935), the German Karl Erich Correns (1864–1933), and the Austrian Erich Tschermak von Seysenegg (1836–1937). Great credit is due to Mendel, but it is by no means correct that the rise which began in 1900 was really due to him; indeed some of the motivation of the American zoologist Thomas Hunt Morgan (1866–1945) resulted from his temporary conviction that Mendel had at least in part gone wrong, so that it was important critically to check his work. Edmund Beecher Wilson (1856–1939), also an American, had published *The Cell in Development and Inheritance*,[1] and by that time the groundwork had already been laid for the great advances in cytology and genetics that followed.

What has happened since then is more than a volume could recount. Genetics, which started at the level of the single organism, has moved down to the molecular level and up to the population level. Evolution has been revitalized, and has become an essentially new, powerful, synthesizing theory. The whole spectacular field of molecular biology has burst on us. Indeed the major scientific concept of the century is that coding of biological information occurs in giant molecular polymers of which one, DNA (deoxyribose nucleic acid), is capable of storing the genetic information and is also capable of self-replication so that the genetic information may be passed on from generation to generation.

The determination of the detailed double-spiral structure of DNA in 1953 was doubtless one of the greatest triumphs that science has ever achieved. To crown this, recent work has almost completely explained the detailed way in which triplets of nucleotides in the DNA molecule control the biochemical activities which lead to the synthesis of the proteins which the genetic material—the DNA—specifies.

These results are so far-reaching that there are those who consider that molecular biology now has left before it, as a challenge to its future, only the mopping-up of a few details of the genetic process.

Others, and I am confident that they are correct, see molecular biology moving on to even greater triumphs. There seems every reasonable prospect that we will, before long, understand immunological reactions at a detailed and in fact molecular level. We must also discover, and doubtless we will, the ways in which differentiation occurs—the detailed controls that provide that certain cells become liver cells whereas others acquire the characteristics that enable them to form other parts of the body.

One of the most exciting prospects for molecular biology is that it will in the next decades give us some real understanding of the functioning of the central nervous system—how do we learn, how do we remember, why do we forget?

Indeed it seems to many scientists, and perhaps to most molecular biologists, that any well-posed question about a living organism can be, and eventually will be, answered in the language of physics and chemistry.

The dramatic period for the physical sciences almost surely was the first few decades of the present century. It seems probable that the equally dramatic period for the biological sciences will be the next few decades. To come back to the theme of my good luck in timing, I had a chance to observe all of the former period, and I am now having the exhilarating chance to observe at least the opening stages of the second period. I have also had the good luck to live through the most vigorous period that science has ever had. The great forward surge of science during my lifetime is highlighted by the estimate that of all the scientists who have ever lived, some 95 per cent are alive today. That the surge continues at an ever-increasing pace is further emphasized by the estimate that of all the words ever written on scientific topics, some 15 per cent were written in the year 1967.

10. Some Limitations of Science

Throughout my life my preoccupation has been with science, but I also have a lifelong concern for and interest in religion. In this, and in the next and final chapter of this book I want to turn aside from the consideration of the incidents of my life, and state some ideas about science and about the relationship between science and religion.

As a necessary background for the discussion of the last-named topic, there are certain aspects of science which must be examined.

I should make it clear at the outset that by the word "science" I mean, of course, real science, basic science, such as physics, chemistry, biology, mathematics, and astronomy. I am not at all talking about the technology that is sometimes mistakenly referred to as scientific; and I am most emphatically not talking about the grotesque views of Madison Avenue which sometimes identify science with gadgetry, resulting in such awful bloopers as "Science produces a new vibrating toothbrush."

Science is an activity, not a catalogue of facts. Scientific curiosity, as the English mathematician and philosopher Alfred North Whitehead (1861–1947) said, ". . . is a passion for an ordered intellectual vision of the connection of events." [1] There is no single fixed and codified set of pro-

154

cedures which constitutes "the scientific method": in contrast, the activity known as science makes use of a highly varied and evolving set of procedures. As the educator James B. Conant has written, "there are many techniques, many ways of stating problems, many methods of analysis." [2] The procedures of science sometimes make use of exceedingly complicated devices, and they are often guided by theoretical ideas which are expressed in a specialized vocabulary and which are based on concepts often profound and abstract. Therefore the scientific endeavor may appear esoteric, if indeed not incomprehensible, to the nonscientist.

But this is, at least to a great extent, an artifact. For the procedures of science are but refinements of the ways in which all men have, from the earliest days of the race, dealt with their environment. When primitive man learned to chip and fashion a stone to make a crude tool, he was being scientific. Suppose a house owner is confronted by a window that sticks. If he reacts by jerking it so hard that his back hurts, or by hitting it a terrible lick with a hammer, then he is being very human but not scientific. If he stops to think, examines it carefully to see if it is jammed crookedly in the frame, or if he remembers that the house has been recently painted and goes to get a sharp blade to cut free the paint seal—then he is being scientific. First the problem must be clearly recognized; decisions must be made as to what is relevant; hypotheses must be formulated and tested. It is a good many steps from freeing a stuck window to building a linear accelerator, but they are all similar steps, which can be taken one after another.

Science deals almost exclusively with the repetitive parts of our experience—with the regularities and uniformities of nature and with things that happen (or could hap-

pen) to everyone. Our lives, however, are often most significantly affected by things which happen only once and only
to us. Unique events such as the nonrecurrent chance to
make an important decision are often those of most significance to us individually, whereas such unique events as the
advent of a Martin Luther or a Shakespeare or a Hitler
are of great importance to us all collectively. Science has
little or nothing to say about these single chances.

It is customary to credit science with "explaining"
phenomena, and this is certainly assumed to be a great and
comforting feat. But in so far as explanation is supposed
to bring to light and exhibit in clear focus the real inner
reason why things behave as they do, then the successes of
science afford little comfort.

For—at least as far as I can see—science has only two
procedures of "explanation" and they are both, in any strict
logical sense, frauds. One of these procedures consists of
remarks which really say: "This phenomenon X which
puzzles you should no longer do so; for it is closely like a
phenomenon Y with which you have long been familiar."
The strange fact is that one need not really understand Y.
He only needs to have been familiar with it for a long
enough time so that he has the (fuzzy and unanalyzed)
conviction that he understands it.

This is explanation by simile, and it is both strangely
satisfying and practically useful. This is what happens when
a scientist says, "Radio waves spread out, die off, are inter-
fered with, like the expanding ripples when a stone is
thrown into a pond." This is what happens when a scientist
says, "The electrons in an atom revolve around the nucleus
as do the planets around the sun."

These explanations by simile are not trivial. Not only

do they bring the personal satisfaction of one who says, "You know, I didn't understand that at all before, and now I do"; they also furnish an important motivation within science as did, in the nineteenth century, the extensive simile comparing electrical quantities and actions with mechanical quantities and actions. But from any fundamental point of view, explanation of this variety, however comforting and useful it may be, is not really explanation. To say that the voltage that "causes" electricity to flow in a wire is like the pressure that causes water to flow in a pipe is very helpful and comforting to a person who is just establishing acquaintance with electricity, and who has for so long seen water flowing in a pipe that he thinks he understands why the pressure causes this; but it is certainly no ultimate explanation.

The second procedure of explanation is very different in character. It is exhibited in pure form in mathematics and theoretical physics. A statement is established by logical derivation from one or more previously established statements. They in turn have been established from a second prior set. One backs down a sort of logical staircase, the statements on each step having been proved by those on the next lower step. If one backs all the way down this stairway he eventually lands on a step which in our modern view does not bear the caption (which Euclid might have written there); "These statements are self-evidently true," but rather bears the candid caption, "This is as far down as we presently go: the statements on this level are pure assumption."

So this second kind of explanation, like the first, does not furnish any ultimate explanation. Both kinds, or mixtures of them, end either in the illusion of familiarity that makes one content to drop the effort, or in the bafflement of pure assumption. The first kind of explanation is not the private property of science. Robert Frost, in his "Education by Poetry," stated that he "believed that metaphor, analogy, the perception of one thing in another, are at the root of understanding itself." [3]

Science is largely concerned with measurable phenomena, and with those aspects of experience which can usefully be dealt with by analytical and logical procedures. It is extremely good at dealing with these. But science cannot decide between a lovely poem and a stupid one. It cannot interpret a sonnet or a symphony. It cannot analyze compassion, or patience, or tolerance, or gentleness. It does not understand intuition, or shrewdness, or wisdom. Even in the realm where it is most successful, it answers *how,* but it never answers *why.*

Science is commonly supposed to unearth and confirm things or statements known as "facts"; but this remark deserves examination. First, the "confirmations" are (with the possible exception of trivial cases) based on measurements or other observations which are not exact in any ultimate sense, and which can therefore really only be stated in terms of probabilities. This reminder is particularly important for those scientists who believe that all empirical matters of fact "boil down to meter readings," since these meter readings are always subject to error.

Furthermore, the character of the "confirmation" of a scientific theory is itself curious, and its degree of finality is often if not usually exaggerated. When one has carried out an experiment to test a theory, the most he can really say is: to a stated degree of accuracy, the theory worked this time. The confirmation can never be absolutely precise (because error in measurement is inescapable), and it can never be complete (because there always remain tests not carried out). Sir Karl R. Popper, one of the leading experts in the philosophy of science, argued in various of his writings years ago the proposition that a scientific theory can, in sober fact, never be confirmed. He was of the opinion that the most one can hope for is that a scientific theory can be *disproved*. More recently Sir Karl has come to the carefully argued conclusion that even this is too much to hope for. In a strict and ultimate sense, a scientific theory can be neither proved true nor proved untrue.

This of course profoundly affects the character of the findings of science. Sir Karl has written:

"Science is not a system of certain, or well-established, statements; nor is it a system which steadily advances towards a state of finality. Our science is not knowledge (*epistēmē*): it can never claim to have attained truth, or even a substitute for it, such as probability. . . .

"The old scientific ideal of *epistēmē*—of absolutely certain, demonstrable knowledge—has proved to be an idol. The demand for scientific objectivity makes it inevitable that every scientific statement remain *tentative forever*. It may indeed be corroborated, but even corroboration is relative to other statements which again are tentative. Only in our subjective experiences of conviction, in our subjective faith, can we be 'absolutely certain.' " [4] This statement will undoubtedly shock those who have a naïve respect for science.

As to logic, everyone, I suppose, thinks of science as the most logical of all fields of human activity, and indeed this characterization is deserved. This use of disciplined reasoning does protect science from careless superficial errors, but it cannot furnish the austere finality, inescapability, and perfection that most people think are automatically assured by logic.

For during recent years some profound and really shocking inner flaws have been revealed in logic. I do not refer to inductive logic, the branch of reasoning that examines all the observed cases recorded in the experimental evidence and seeks to induce therefrom general laws. This is how the mind of man attempts to reach universals by the study of particulars. Inductive logic has been, and remains, something of a scandal ever since David Hume denied its propriety over two hundred years ago.

I refer to deductive logic—the unrolling through carefully controlled reasoning of the statements that follow from a body of assumed postulates. This branch of reasoning, which is at the core of theoretical science, has recently undergone penetrating analysis, and two previously unexpected difficulties have been uncovered. First, it has been shown that it is impossible (not just unpleasantly difficult, but *impossible*) to decide, relative to a set of postulates which has been adopted as the basis for a theory, whether or not any such set of assumptions rich enough to lead to a significant theory is or is not internally consistent. Thus, at the very central core of any theory, there may be an undiscoverable flaw. And second, it has been shown that any postulational theory is necessarily incomplete, in the sense that it is always possible to ask, within the system, questions that cannot be answered.

Underlying the phrase "scientific statement of a fact" is a complex substratum of assumptions and agreements, some of them pushed down so low in the basement complex of past experience as to be out of sight and forgotten, and all of them subject to the limitations inherent in the foundations of logic. At the best, the "facts" of science represent a high level of agreement (at least within the culture in question) concerning the measured confirmations of scientific theories which are themselves based on chains of hypotheses, the more basic of which turn out, on honest examination, to be pure (or should I say impure?) assumption.

As we will see in a moment, if one makes a different start in the basic assumptions, has a different sense as to what are useful questions and satisfying answers, adopts a different system of metaphysics and a different world outlook, then he ends up with a quite different set of "facts."

There is no intention here to denigrate the usefulness of the ordinary working understandings as to the facts of science. Indeed without these (almost completely submerged) agreements, scientists could not get forward with their daily work. The game is a completely absorbing and highly rewarding one, but it is nevertheless a game. It is important to recognize that there are other games to play which start from other premises, have other rules, and come out with other sorts of results. Anyone has a right to play the game or games of his own choosing; but he does not have the right to view his own game as the only one, or as the ultimately preferred one.

Even within the professional framework of Western science, what is a fact today need not be a fact tomorrow. There was a time when any competent scientist would have confidently affirmed, "Mass is always conserved." He would also have said, "Energy is always conserved." These two rules which worked so well under such a wide range of circumstances are now, of course, replaced by a new rule which states that it is a fact that mass can be converted into energy or energy into mass (according to the Einstein formula $E = mc^2$), and what is conserved is not either separately, but rather the properly calculated sum of the two.

Thomas S. Kuhn, professor of the History of Science at Princeton University, analyzes the fascinating way in which science operates for a time on the basis of a certain standard and approved set of procedures, then is confronted by a crisis, and then shifts "the network of theory through which it deals with the world." [5] These shifts, these scientific revolutions, are certainly not to be viewed as lamentable periods in the history of science. On the contrary, these are the great moments. Science responds nobly to challenge, just as Arnold Toynbee has pointed out is the case in social and political history. The point not to be missed here is that science does profoundly change, and by that very process shows that it never was the guardian of ultimate fact, and can indeed never be.

Any person who takes the smugly confident attitude that science (*his* science of course) has unique capacity for discovering ultimate and permanent "facts" should read some of the essays of the great American student of linguistics, Benjamin Lee Whorf (1897–1941).[6]

Whorf's argument goes like this: Those of us who are immersed in Western culture and whose competence in communication is restricted to the Indo-European languages are usually totally unaware of the deep submerged assumptions which, in a completely interlocked way, control our language, our modes of thinking, our inherent ideas as to what is natural and important, the way we dissect experience, and our general views about the realities of the universe in which we exist. We are as unconscious of these linguistic-cultural-conceptual restraints as a fish is unconscious of water.

Only by a dedicated and prolonged study that gives one some approximation to understanding the linguistic-cultural-conceptual framework of some other group of people is it possible to begin to have an externalized view of ourselves.

For example, the Hopi Indians have ideas about time, space, and motion quite unlike those we consider so obvious and necessary. In particular, they "have no general notion or intuition of TIME as a smooth flowing continuum. . . ." In the Hopi view "time disappears and space is altered . . . new concepts and abstractions flow into the picture, taking up the task of describing the universe without reference to such time or space." Our language has no terms, indeed no grammar, which is adequate to express the Hopi abstractions. In reverse, the Hopis are doubtless confused by the way we act, and think, and talk. Their difficulty in dealing with us is at least hinted at by the fact that their verbs have no tenses. Many conceptual entities for which we have nouns (such as lightning, wave, flame, puff of smoke) are not dealt with in their language by nouns but rather by verbs. They have a metaphysics of their own, and deal with experience and reality in ways that are quite unlike ours, but which nevertheless work entirely satisfactorily for them.

In some older views, talking was supposed merely to be the external expression of what had previously been formulated nonlinguistically, "formulation" being an independent process to be called "thought" or "thinking." If that view were significantly valid, then *thought* might not depend on grammar but on something to be called the "laws of logic or reason," supposed to be the same for all observers of the universe and hence to represent a basic and universal rationale. Even if this were a correct view, it would still be true that all agreements between persons are reached by linguistic processes. If A and B are to understand each other and are to "agree," they must necessarily share (even if unsuspectingly) an amazingly complex system of linguistic patterns and classifications.

Whorf, moreover, was convinced by his studies that thinking, even if it can in fact proceed without words, is not free from linguistic control. The "background linguistic system (in other words the grammar) of each language is not merely a reproducing system for voicing ideas, but rather is itself a shaper of ideas, the program and guide for the individual's mental activity, for his analysis of impressions, for his synthesis of his mental stock in trade . . . we dissect nature along lines laid down by our natural languages . . . we cut nature up, organize it into concepts, and ascribe significances as we do, largely because we are parties to an agreement to organize it in this way—an agreement that holds throughout our speech community and is codified in the patterns of our language. The agreement is of course an implicit and unstated one BUT ITS TERMS ARE ABSOLUTELY OBLIGATORY: we cannot talk at all except by subscribing to the organization and clarification of data which the agreement decrees."

In previous passages we have seen that science cannot be viewed as perfect and permanent. The excursion into linguistic considerations greatly enlarges our view. Not only does *our* science have very human weaknesses; our science is only one example of what a "science" can be. There can be and are others, so fundamentally different that anyone must devote years of study before he has learned enough to begin to understand and appreciate the alternatives.

I am sure that some readers will react by thinking: It is curious and somewhat interesting that the Hopi Indians do not share our grammar, our ideas, and our way of dealing with experience. But after all, let's not be too impressed! Look at the Hopi Indians! Did they ever cure a disease, or prove a theorem, or invent television?

These questions cannot be reasonably posed in this way. Indeed a Hopi Indian (excluding those who have shifted over into our culture) would undoubtedly fail to understand these queries and would probably feel sorry for the questioner.

The Hopi Indians, moreover, have been used here as an example simply because Whorf studied them so long and so profoundly that he could, at least in some measure, bridge the gap between them and us. Whorf takes us a little way out on that bridge and gives us glimpses of the strange land on the other side. There are, of course, many other cultures that could be used as examples—Semitic, Tibetan, African—if only each of these had its Whorf. Modern Chinese and Turkish scientists, as Whorf mentions, describe the world in the same terms as Western scientists. That they do so "means, of course, only that they have taken over bodily the entire Western system of rationalizations, not that they have corroborated that system from their native posts of observation." I have a Turkish biochemist friend who writes me, from Istanbul, letters which could as well be postmarked Cambridge (Massachusetts or England).

And there are other examples. The distinguished English biochemist and Orientalist Joseph Needham has devoted years to the study of Chinese language and culture, and he is producing an heroic series of volumes on the older "non-Western" aspects of Chinese science. Writing about Needham's great works, an English-trained Yale professor of history of science has said, "There can be no doubt that Chinese science and technology have been just as inventive, just as good, just as bad, as the science and technology of the ancient and medieval West." [7]

The moment one realizes that our views about the realities of the world about us and the way in which we dissect experience are controlled by unrecognized linguistic-cultural restraints, then he also realizes that man, in attempting to understand the universe, inescapably tries to deal with it in his own terms. Man is what he is, and taking thought will not permit him to be submicroscopically small any more than it will add cubits to his stature.

Of the two basic physical entities of length and time, man quite naturally, in the early and unsophisticated stages of science, drew upon his own direct personal experience. A cubit is the distance from the tip of the elbow to the end of the middle finger. A span is the distance, when the hand is fully extended, from the end of the thumb to the end of the little finger. The dimensions of the adult human body are, very roughly, 200 centimeters in height, roughly 66 centimeters in width across the shoulders, and roughly 35 centimeters in thickness through the chest. The average of these three basic human dimensions is about 100 centimeters; so that this distance of 100 centimeters, or 1 meter, is one of which each human being has a direct personal comprehension. It is, within our anthromorphically controlled culture, perfectly natural, simple, and directly meaningful to talk about a distance of 100 centimeters, or of any mild multiple or submultiple thereof, such as 50 meters or one fiftieth of a meter. But, except to the scientist, such phrases as "6 billion billion meters" and "a billionth of a billionth of a meter" simply have no natural, homely, direct meaning. Such language is not part of our normal linguistic usage, since our culture does not have any normal and frequent contact with such distances. From the point of view of familiar "man-sized" dimensions, a billion billion meters and a billionth of a billionth of a meter are completely exotic, totally removed from our normal experience.

Man's immediate experience with extension in space varies from, say, the size of a needle point used to pick out a thorn in his finger to, say, the circumference of the earth— a range from about 10^{-2} centimeters to about 10^9 centimeters.* It's all very well to ask him to look at the moon or the sun and imagine how far away they are: the plain country fact is that he can't imagine those distances, for he has had (until recent astronautical flights) no tangible experience with them. Man can, to be sure, extend his sight by looking through a telescope or a microscope, but what he really sees —the image examined by his eyes—is still some "reasonable-sized" object.

In his experience with time there are similar limitations. Years, days, hours, minutes, seconds—these are di-

* I will express all quantities, as scientists tend to do, in centimeter-gram-second units. For any reader not familiar with exponential notation, it is necessary only to know that 10^5, for example, means 1 followed by 5 zeroes: thus it is an abbreviation for 100,000. Similarly 10^7 means 10,000,000, or 10 million, 10^9 means 1 billion, and 10^{18} 1 billion billion. To express small numbers, 10^{-5} is 1 divided by 10^5, and is thus equal to 0.00001.

rectly experienced. Indeed, as he watches a close play at first base, the umpire may have to distinguish the time order of two events (the arrival of the ball in the first baseman's mitt and the touching of the base by the runner's foot) which may be separated by as little as one or two hundredths of a second. This is about as "fine" as one can sharpen his direct sense of time and is slightly finer-grained than our ordinary appreciation of time events—the reaction time of individuals averages a few hundredths of a second. (I may be in mild error in some of these estimates, but that does not affect my conclusions.) Thus our direct experience with time ranges from roughly 10^{-2} seconds to about 10^9 seconds*—which rather curiously comes out the same as the range for distance.

With experimental equipment to extend his senses, man has vastly increased the ranges stated. A reasonable upper limit for length is the estimate of the so-called diameter of the universe. This is of the order of 10^{10} light-years,† or 10^{28} centimeters.

As to very small lengths, it is noteworthy that Coulomb's Law for the force acting between two electrical charges was verified in 1911 for distances as small as 10^{-12} centimeters, in 1933 for distances down to 10^{-13} centimeters, and in 1954 for distances down to 10^{-14} centimeters. For an experimentalist, the lower limit of length appears at the moment to be 10^{-15} centimeters, which is the wavelength associated with a 30 Bev accelerator, the largest now operating. This figure will be reduced to 10^{-17} when the

*This is roughly the average number of seconds from the birth of a man to the birth of his offspring—a "generation" of time.

†A light-year is the distance that light, traveling at 186,000 miles per second, goes in one year. I once heard it defined by a student as "a year in which very few stars are discovered."

200 Bev accelerator at Weston, Illinois, has been successfully completed.

At least one theoretical physicist, however, dares to contemplate distances which are many, many times more fine-grained than those dealt with by the experimentalists. Professor John A. Wheeler of Princeton, the physicist who was so closely and importantly associated with Niels Bohr during the atomic fission days, has elaborated an imaginative and daring theory of the "geometrodynamics" of empty, curved superspace, which views larger-scale entities such as electric charges as being the manifestation, up at the level of 10^{-15} or larger, of topological characteristics of multiply connected superspace. Wheeler's theory involves what he calls "the Planck distance" which is numerically equal to the square root of $\hbar G/c^3$, $\hbar$ being the Planck constant for angular momentum, G the gravitational constant, and c the speed of light. This Planck's distance[8] has the value of 1.6×10^{-33} centimeters, and is the distance within which quantum fluctuations of a typical gravitational potential are appreciable.

This "Planck's distance," of the order of 10^{-33} centimeters, is, as far as I know, the smallest distance which has as yet been contemplated in physical theory.

As to the maximum range of times that enter into modern theories, this extends from the half-life of the most evanescent particles—something of the order of 10^{-16} seconds, up to the estimates of the age of the galaxies—say, 10^{17} seconds.

Thus instrumental and theoretical extensions have pushed the realm of small distance down some 10^{-13} (the reciprocal of 10 million million) times, or perhaps even down 10^{-31} times, as compared with the smallness directly accessible to our senses; and have pushed the realm of large distances up some 10^{18} (a billion billion) times, as compared with the largeness with which we have direct experience. For time, as contrasted with space, the corresponding factors are 10^{-14} and 10^8.

Is this much condensation and stretching of man's immediate experience meaningful? One's first reaction is to say that we must trust science, and whereas it may indeed be difficult—or even impossible—to imagine the smallness and the largeness of these numbers, we must nevertheless accept them.

This disregards, it seems to me, the necessarily anthropomorphic character of all man's activities and concepts. It may easily be that our scientific concepts are wholly inapplicable when the scale of events is made so infinitesimally small, or so astronomically large. It may be, indeed, that our language, our syntax, and our logic are all so locked into our experience, our necessarily man-sized experience, that they are useless at these extreme scales. When the theoretical physicists tell us that the density in nuclei may be as high as 10,000 million tons per cubic inch, and ask, "Is that not surprising and wonderful?" we should in fact reply, "No, on the contrary I think the particular sounds you just made are meaningless. And when you talk about 'the diameter of the universe,' I think that those words are nonsensical also."

If it indeed is the case that our man-size, average-size concepts are inapplicable to the description of the indefinitely small world inside the nucleus of an atom, how could one possibly have a theory for structure and events at that level? If we truly believe that elementary events—that is, events in which the actors are elementary particles—are basic, and that all the rest is statistical elaboration, then we should not start in the middle and try to work in both directions; we should start at the bottom and work up.

It was considerations such as these which led Max Mason and myself, early in the 1920s, to try to think about a wholly new starting point for physical theories. It was our idea that in the ultimately small world there would be nothing corresponding to our ordinary concepts of distance or of time, these being supposedly inappropriate for unitary events. At some mature stage of the theory certain quantities would emerge, probably as statistical averages of unitary quantities, and among those emergent large-scale quantities would be one which would be recognized to correspond to our ordinary gross concept of distance—another to our ordinary gross concept of time. This might be similar to the situation with respect to the pressure exerted by a gas. When one descends to the molecular level there is nothing that can be called "pressure": the individual molecules are flying about helter-skelter, colliding with one another in all types of glancing or direct encounters. When one analyzes the totality of these collisions, the large-scale concept of pressure emerges, built up out of the average effect of all the collisions. And this large-scale quantity, pressure, can be thus demonstrated to depend in a smooth and predictable way upon other large-scale quantities such as "temperature" which also have emerged as statistical averages of smaller-scale events.

Unfortunately, it seems to be the case that ultimate theories must be built "up," not "down." That is, it does not seem possible to break up the large-scale averaged quantities into meaningful bits, for we simply have no idea what those bits are. The kinetic theory of gases, which explains the properties and behavior of gases in terms of the motions of the particles composing the gas, appears to contradict this remark, but the fact is that kinetic theory is not an ultimate theory: it is a two-stage large-scale theory. The "molecules" of kinetic gas theory are really not unitary objects, but a surprisingly successful imaginary substitute therefor—tiny elastic perfect spheres; and kinetic theory is therefore in actuality not really a good illustration of what I am talking about. Kinetic theory is a successful instance of a theory which successfully descends on two steps of a macroscopic scale, whereas our position was that the ultimate theory of matter must start at the bottom, as regards scale, and then ascend.

This, however, forces one starkly to confront the difficulty. Our man-sized experiences have given us no concepts, no words, no syntax, no logic suitable to the scale of these events. How does one get started with such a theory?

If I knew the answer to that question, I would be writing another book, not this one. But I continue to be convinced that a proper theory of ultimately small affairs cannot successfully penetrate down to that level, drilling from above, but must arise within those affairs. That quantum theory does penetrate from above, using the linguistic machinery of the man-sized world to describe the microworld is, in my judgment, its basic weakness and the origin of its internal contradictions and of the general messiness of the theory. I realize that my esthetic dislike of quantum theory should be canceled out and translated into admiration by the magnificent sweep of the detailed successes of the theory. But try as I will, I cannot change my stubborn prejudice.

Ideas of the sort advanced here are expressed from

time to time by some of the ablest physicists. John A. Wheeler entitled his address as the retiring president of the American Physical Society "The End of Time." The news report of this lecture contained the remark "Is there a scale of distances and events so small that time loses its meaning?" "On the very-small-distance scale," said Dr. Wheeler, "there would be no such thing as before and after."

In 1963, Geoffrey F. Chew of the Department of Physics of the University of California at Berkeley wrote a paper in which he said: "Twentieth century physics already has undergone two breath-taking revolutions—in relativity and in quantum mechanics. We are standing on the threshold of a third." [9]

At the stage of going over the manuscript of this book for the final time, one more piece of evidence has come to the surface. This, to my great delight, comes from a poet!

In the opening poem of *The Blue Swallows,* Howard Nemerov says:

> Below the ten thousand billionth of a
>   centimeter
> Length ceases to exist. Beyond three
>   billion light years
> The nebulae would have to exceed the
>   speed of light
> In order to be, which is impossible:
>   no universe.
> The long and short of it seems to be
>   that thought
> Can make itself unthinkable . . .[10]

11. Science, Contradiction, and Religion

For the main conclusions of this final chapter, it is necessary for us to consider at this point a concept, a principle, that was scientific in its origin but which is now recognized to have a much wider significance. This is the concept of complementarity.

The principle of complementarity was first enunciated by Niels Bohr in 1928. The development of the ideas and the debate that clarified the issues were participated in by many of the great scientific figures of that fantastically active and exciting period. In particular, both of the two most important scientific leaders of those days, Bohr and Einstein, were intimately and intensely involved.

In the years just preceding 1928 some upsetting notions had come to the surface. All of them, of course, were consequences of the earlier revolutionary idea of Max Planck that energy is not continuously divisible, but that it always occurs in discrete packets of a precisely specified minimum size.

One set of these ideas was concerned with the fact that quantum theory could be formulated in two different (but as it eventually turned out, analytically equivalent) ways, one of which involved talking about *discrete particles*

174

(which, since Planck, seemed rather to be the way the theory ought to go), and the other of which (due to Schrödinger but going back to ideas advanced by the French physicist Louis Victor de Broglie a few years earlier) was expressed in terms of *continuous waves*. The status and interrelationship of these two approaches was a critical issue when it became evident—experimentally evident—that such a basic entity as a photon of light had to be treated under some circumstances as if it were in fact wavelike, but under other circumstances as though it were particle-like. The same embarrassing duality was soon found to apply to electrons. Previously always thought of as "particles," electrons now also had to be admitted to be wavelike under some circumstances.

At about this same time (February 1927) the brilliant young German physicist Werner Heisenberg developed— and showed the necessity of—the idea that it was impossible experimentally to obtain precise information on *both* the position and the velocity of a particle. There was a joint uncertainty in the two sets of measurements: as the experimenter made his determination of one of the two quantities (either position or velocity) more and more precise, the error in any simultaneous determination of the other became bigger and bigger. This arose because of the fact, neglected for so long, that an observation necessarily affected the thing observed. This effect is ordinarily of no importance, being negligibly small, when the thing under observation is of substantial size and mass, but it is critically important when observing elementary particles.

To measure position more and more precisely, the experimenter might reflect from the particle in question a more and more energetic pulse of radiant energy; but as this pulse is made more and more intense, it has a greater and greater disturbing effect on the velocity of the particle. To put it roughly, if you bounce off enough energy to tell you precisely where the particle *was*, the rebound imparts so much unknown velocity to the particle that you don't know much about how it is moving, and hence about where it now is. This joint uncertainty was not only characteristic of the pair of quantities' position and velocity, but applied equally to various other pairs of quantities which entered into physical theory.*

Bohr found these ideas so stimulating that he pursued them with what Heisenberg described as "almost terrifying relentlessness." Bohr, moreover, considered the wave-particle dualism to be so central a phenomenon that he was convinced that it must be taken as a starting point for any interpretation of the theoretical and experimental exploration of physics.

Previous natural philosophy had been based on the assumption (which Bohr himself remarked was "inherent in ordinary conventions of language") that one can successfully distinguish between the behavior of objects and the means used to observe that behavior. But in dealing with atomic and other very fine-scaled processes one has to face and take account of the fact that the measuring and observing procedures have a determining influence on the thing being observed, so that "property observed" and "means of observation" are inescapably related.

At the descriptive level at which the experimenter tells what he has done and seeks to persuade his colleagues to

---

* In quantum theory, such pairs are called "canonically conjugate"; another example, in addition to the pair position and velocity, is the pair energy and time.

agreement, he is forced to use the classical terms of large-scale physics and the ordinary linguistic machinery our Western culture has developed. On the other hand, it is necessary to recognize that experiments concerning phenomena which are not included within the range of classical physics cannot be interpreted as giving information about inherent and independent properties of the objects under study, but can only give information which relates to the inseparable combination "object plus procedure of observation."

These considerations led Bohr to conclude that the information obtained about an object by using one set of experimental conditions of observation should not be expected to be the same as, or necessarily consistent with, the information obtained when using a different set of observational procedures. If the second set of observational conditions excludes the first set, then the information obtained by using one set must be viewed as *complementary* to the information obtained by using the other observational procedure. However contradictory the two sets of information may appear to be, they must be accepted as equally valid. It is not only futile, it is essentially meaningless to try to decide whether electrons are particles or are wavelike. Under one set of observational circumstances, electrons must be considered to be particles, and under other observational circumstances, they must be considered to be wavelike. By accepting the two contradictory descriptions and using each under appropriate circumstances, one has a richer and more satisfying concept than is furnished by either description taken alone.

Commenting on the principle, Bohr stated that ". . . any given application of classical concepts precludes the simultaneous use of other classical concepts, which in a different connection are equally necessary for the elucidation of the phenomena." As this quotation shows, Bohr himself clearly recognized the linguistic aspects of the situation. "From his early youth," one of his friends and colleagues has written, "Bohr had been preoccupied by this problem of the ambiguity of language." [1] In his essay "Quantum Theory and Its Implications," Heisenberg describes an expedition on Bohr's sailing boat, carried out by a group of scientists at Copenhagen. "Bohr was full of the new interpretation of quantum theory, and as the boat took us full sail southward in the sunshine, there was plenty of time to tell of this scientific event, and to reflect philosophically on the nature of atomic theory. *Bohr began by talking of the difficulties of language* . . . [my italics]." Heisenberg also remarks, "This concept of complementarity fitted well the fundamental philosophical attitude which he [Bohr] had always had, and in which the limitations of our means of expressing ourselves entered as a central philosophical problem." [2]

In view of what we have noted earlier concerning Whorf's analysis of the relationship between grammar, culture, and science, and because of what I myself want to say later, it is important to emphasize just what circumstance is responsible for the emergence of Bohr's Principle of Complementarity.

It is meaningless to assert that nature "really has" contradictory aspects ("an electron *is* both a particle and a wave"). The dilemma arises because we necessarily formulate the results of fine-scaled experiments in the traditional language suited to large-scale, or let us rather say man-sized, experience. When experiments concern man-sized objects and events (as in rolling a sphere down an inclined plane to study the dynamics of ordinary things), the traditionally phrased descriptions of varied experiments are all consistent, one with another. When the experiment dips down into the "little world" of atomic and nuclear affairs, but our language of description and agreement remains at the traditional level of man-sized concepts, then the contradictions arise. It is as though one anthropologist observes a Hopi prayer dance carried out under one set of circumstances, and a second anthropologist observes a Hopi prayer dance carried out under another set of circumstances. Each of the two anthropologists writes his interpretation, in English, of what he has observed and heard. The descriptions are inconsistent, and no wonder.

If we could some day develop a set of concepts, and the necessary linguistic tools, to approach the "little world" from below, rather than descending on it from above, then scientists might create a subculture, with its appropriate linguistic apparatus, within which would be completely lacking the hybrid contradictions with which complementarity deals.

It seems to me that this reasoning can be extended to another realm of physics. Just as the nuclear physicist uses man-sized concepts and traditional language in his efforts to describe events in the tiny world of scale less than 10^{-15} cubic centimeters, so the astrophysicist uses the same man-sized concepts and language in his attempt to describe cosmic phenomena whose scale is of the order of 10^{28} cubic centimeters. He comes to two different ideas about, for example, the "origin of the universe." Did it arise as a "big bang," or did it evolve in a systematic procedure which may be part of a rhythmic process of expanding and receding? Or could it be that these two views are complementary, each valid when the questions are asked in the appropriate way, and both necessary for a complete description? For our man-sized language may well be as inadequate at the cosmic scale as at the subatomic scale.

The concept of complementarity has often been extended far beyond the circumstances that led to its enunciation. Bohr himself called attention to problems in psychology and in biology that present complementary aspects. He considered that a complementary relationship often obtained between "thoughts" and "feelings," since if we analyze our emotions, we scarcely possess them any more; and that "instinct" and "reason" may well also form a complementary pair. He pointed out that a biological experiment aimed at illuminating the concept "life" can very well be an experiment that destroys the life of the organism under study. A complete description of a personal relationship may well involve complementary statements, some of which, made within one context, are phrased entirely in terms of love, and others, within a different context, being phrased in terms of hate.

It may be helpful for the reader to look at a very simple and specific example, which further illustrates the concept of complementarity.

In the case of the simple functional relationship mathematically expressed by the equation $y = x^2$, if you substitute the integer $+4$ for x, then you get a single value, namely $+16$, for y. But a different situation arises if we consider the relationship $y = \sqrt{x}$. For if we set $x = +4$, there now are *two* answers, since the square root of $+4$ is either $+2$ or -2. Either number, when multiplied by itself, gives $+4$.

If a person is interested in positive numbers and asks

"What is the square root of +4?" the answer is of course +2. If another person is interested in negative numbers, and asks the same question, the answer is −2. If a third person takes a more embracing view, the answer is that both +2 and −2 are square roots of +4. The third person has a richer and more rewarding total reply, even though the two parts of it are inconsistent.

Several of the comments I have made about the nature of the scientific enterprise may well be judged to be deflating if indeed not derogatory, for I have said that science deals only with very limited aspects of our total experience; that science is never perfect, never final, never fully confirmed; that science does not really "explain," and indeed never even attempts to answer the query "How?"; that the fundamental assumptions on which theoretical science is based are subject to the limitations imposed by the flaws which exist in the foundations of deductive logic; that modern Western science is by no means a unique invention; that, indeed, the science at any time and place is essentially determined by the interlocked metaphysics and linguistic apparatus of the culture in question, and hence depends upon the kind of questions the culture considers it important to ask, the kind of techniques of exploration that are available, the kind of evidence that is judged convincing, and the kinds of answers that are acceptable and rewarding; and that at its very foundations, science has learned that it must accommodate ambiguity, duality, and contradiction.

These points, however they may be judged by those who (quite mistakenly, I think) consider science to be the ultimate and all-powerful source of unchanging knowledge, should be of real comfort to those who (equally mistakenly) have been led to fear science as a relentless mechanical monster. They should be enthusiastically welcomed by those who believe, as I most firmly do, that the scientific enterprise is basically an artistic endeavor, that it has all the freedom of any other imaginative and creative activity, this activity being characterized by very special traditions of disinterested and unprejudiced open-mindedness together with a built-in protection against serious or prolonged error. Science is one of the most mature of the arts, combining a maximum of both freedom and discipline.

These points, moreover, make it clear that science should have no quarrel with the humane arts or with contemplative fields of thought, nor they with science. They are all, each using its characteristic methods, seeking to perceive order and unity in diversity. They are all based on faith, they are all creations of imaginative minds; they are all alive, growing, changing; they all are limited by what our linguistic apparatus and our cultural concepts permit. They all represent high effort on the part of man to savor and appreciate his surroundings, and thus to enrich his life.

The essential unity of the scientific enterprise and the artistic enterprise has been widely recognized by the great scientists. The physicist J. Robert Oppenheimer (1904–1967) described this interrelationship most perceptively when he wrote: "The artist and scientist both live always at the edge of mystery, surrounded by it. Both struggle to make partial order in total chaos. They can, in their work and in their lives, help themselves, help one another, and help all men." [3] It is interesting, I think, to note that this bridge has also been evident to great artists. Dylan Thomas must have recognized all this when he said (as other poets before him had also said), "Beauty is the sense of unity in diversity." [4] I get a very special kick out of being told that the poet W. H. Auden, at sixty, subscribed to but one magazine—and that *Scientific American*!

In a letter he wrote seventy years ago, the Russian dramatist Anton Chekhov said: "I would like people not to see a conflict where there is none. There has always been knowledge in the world. Anatomy and belles-lettres are of equally noble descent; they both have the same purposes and the same enemy—the devil—and there is absolutely no reason for them to fight each other. There is no struggle for survival here. If a man understands the system of blood circulation, he is rich; if in addition he studies the history of religion and learns by heart the poem, 'I recall the miraculous moment,' he will be richer and not poorer; consequently, we are dealing only with positives. That is why geniuses have never fought, and in Goethe the scientist got along beautifully with the poet." [5]

I cannot close my remarks about science without making clear my conviction that the limiting characteristics of the scientific enterprise which I have emphasized paradoxically increase, rather than diminish, its stature. Granting what science sets out to do, granting what it conceptually can do, I think it must be agreed that it is one of the most successful, if indeed not the most successful, activity in which man has ever been engaged. The degree of control over nonliving matter it affords is fantastically well matched to our culture's appetites and demands. There is every reasonable prospect that it will be able to furnish a similar degree of control over many of the aspects of living matter. The picture which this medium paints of the world about us is one of both intricate detail and sweeping splendor. It is a picture of almost incredible beauty.

It will well serve as a transition to what I want to write about religion if I say something at this point about science and value.

There are many (including myself in younger days) who have affirmed that science has nothing to do with value. "Facts," they have said, "are wholly neutral. The scientist discovers facts, and the process of doing so is a totally amoral activity. If someone utilizes these facts in an ugly or immoral way, the fault lies wholly with him."

The testimony of the scientists who established the possibility of making an atomic bomb rather completely demolishes that argument. And everything we have recognized here about the nature of facts, and indeed about the interaction between culture and science, makes it impossible to establish a clean-cut separation between what scientists do (which is what science is), what they think is worth doing, and the criteria which determine worthwhileness. Just as it is impossible to isolate "facts" from their cultural origins, so it is impossible to quarantine facts from their cultural use.

More specifically, there are recognizable value judgments which are part and parcel of the scientific enterprise. The scientist's ideas about interest and importance clearly help to determine what "facts" are brought to the surface and made available for application. The scientist does not stumble and grope his way through nature as would a drunken man in a dark attic, bumping by accident into boxes that he opens and examines. The scientist is motivated and guided by a powerful ethic.

He is deeply convinced, for example, that it is his honorable duty to know all that it is possible to know about the world and its living inhabitants. He understands, with a clarity that is scarcely to be found anywhere else among men's activities, that honesty actually and practically is the best policy. He understands the nature and importance of persuasion and agreement better than does any politician.

Scientists today are broadly recognizing the interrelationships between what they do and the problems and needs of the society of which they are a part. The pages of *Science,* of *Nature,* of the *Bulletin of the Atomic Scientists,* of *Daedalus,* and of many other journals are full of discussions which clearly recognize that science does not operate in a sort of moral germ-free enclosure, but rather that it exists in the world of affairs, of hopes, and of responsibilities, so that the day-by-day decisions of science inescapably involve all sorts of value judgments.

The scientist takes deep satisfaction in being a part of a dedicated world-wide community. His craft teaches him that he must accept a certain kind of evidence, and he does so with humility and with lack of prejudice, even when the evidence is contrary to his expectations and—human as he is —his desires. He is a highly disciplined individual. The distillation of many varied and complicated experiences, and their compact and powerful expression in a theory of broad generality, gives him a great esthetic pleasure. In his scientific work he is strongly influenced by a sense of beauty. He knows just what he means by a good theory or a good experiment, and he has a right to use the word "good."

What I have said about science makes it easier for me to express my ideas about religion. These must, moreover, be *my* ideas. There is sufficient agreement about science so that one can express generally accepted views; but religion is so personal an affair that no one—or at least certainly not I—can speak for others.

Throughout, I will be sustained and liberated by the concept of complementarity. Asking a question from one point of view, I will have one answer. Asking it from another and quite different point of view, I may very well suggest a second answer which is inconsistent with the former, but which can be viewed as complementary to it, the two taken together giving a richer and truer picture than either separately.

First and foremost, I take a liberal position in religion, believing it to be a growing and improving body of thought and precept. I think that religious ideas have matured from primitive notions to the principles of Christ, just a little as science has advanced from the chipping of stone implements to the experimenting of present-day physicists. I sense, however, an important contrast at this point between science and religion. Science is very unlikely to change its outward manifestations (the laws governing gross matter, for example) , but it will almost surely have to alter its inner ideas. Religion, on the other hand, will wish to change some of its superficial aspects (forms of worship, specific dogmas defining moral behavior in modern situations) , but it is very unlikely to have to make any substantial change in its basic and central ideas. In science, to put it differently, certitude lies near the surface, with uncertainty and confusion near the core; with religion, there often is confusion near the surface, but certitude at the core. In Western religion we will never, I believe, have to alter the central principles which Jesus enunciated, although we certainly must continuously reinterpret them to make them applicable to changing problems.

I cannot conscientiously repeat the Apostles' Creed, for it contains sentences which begin with the affirmation, "I believe . . ."; and in fact I do not so believe. I am not in the least concerned with various other formal dogmas, such as the Immaculate Conception, and the Resurrection. If these should turn out to be folk myths, perhaps introduced so that Christianity could compete on even terms with the claims of other religions, this would not disturb me in the least. I do not worry about the divinity of Christ, primarily I suppose because I simply do not have any understanding of what the words mean. The only Trinity that I understand is the trinity of God, my brother, and me. For two reasons I have no interest in the question: Is there a life after death? First, there is no evidence whatsoever which can be brought to bear on this question, so it seems to me a waste of time to consider it. Second, I am too much preoccupied with the challenges of *this* life.

None of the traditional religious dogmas seems to me of importance. What is important to me in the Christian religion is the wisdom and beauty of part of the Old Testament and—on a scale of superlative importance—the teachings of Christ.

I have no interest in the supposed instances of direct revelation. Whatever I believe about God, I cannot think that He bothers to chisel messages on tablets of stone or uses a sort of celestial loudspeaker. Certainly I cannot think of Him as an old gentleman with whiskers who occupies the top level of a three-story universe consisting of hell, earth, and heaven.

As to the Bible, I consider much of it to be a marvelous

human record of divine wisdom. There is some of it that I think God would be pleased to have eliminated. But since it is so clearly a human record, with a vague and complex history for its component parts and for their centuries-long wanderings through a number of languages, I am not in the least surprised or disturbed at the wide range of quality, nor at the textual inconsistencies. The infiltration of folklore, myth, and poetry adds to the interest and charm, without in the least affecting the validity. For those earnest souls who seem to think that God dictated the Bible in English, complete with punctuation, to the committee of churchmen selected by King James in 1611, I have sympathy but not much comprehension.

I do not think that unique access to God is gained through the linguistic apparatus or the concepts of the West. Although I do not have the scholarship to appreciate them, I have every intuitive basis for thinking that the great religious writings of other cultures, and their views concerning their God, have equal validity. They may not seem to me as pure, or as nobly and simply conceived, but that could be my fault, not theirs. I only say that the principles of Jesus are supreme for me.

I think science and religion share certain linguistic difficulties. Just as the man-sized language of science is (at least so I think) entirely unsuitable at both subnuclear and cosmic levels, the necessarily man-sized language of religion is also very often unsuitable. We simply have no words in which to capture God. Some of the poetry of the Bible comes as close to doing so as it is possible to do.

I have, however, made so many disclaimers that I ought to state what positive views I hold which, taken together, constitute my personal religious belief. And at this point I explicitly invoke the principle of complementarity.

When I ask about the nature of God and do this within an impersonalized and somewhat intellectualized framework, I find it satisfying to say that God represents the moral purpose of the universe, and that He is the author of the grand design, ultimately responsible for its intricate beauty and for our evolving capacity to recognize the lovely unity that pervades all the apparent diversity.

On the other hand, when I am in trouble, when I am frightened about the safety of those I love, when I am wrestling with very personal problems, when I hear the cry of a child in the night, or when I am moved by a well-remembered hymn, then my view of God is paradoxically different. Then He is the ever dependable friend, the loving, comforting, and protecting Father. I cannot do better than Tolstoy's affirmation, "I believe in God, who for me is Spirit, Love, the Principle of all things. I believe that He is in me, and I in Him." [6]

If the two concepts—the impersonal abstract one and the emotional and very personal one—seem inconsistent or contradictory, then I repeat that they arise under mutually exclusive circumstances and can strictly be viewed as complementary.

Religion, in my view, has no possible reason to resent or deny the magnificent success with which science deals with the problems that lie within its domain. On the other hand, religion is the main guide for a vaster—and to many, a far more significant—range of problems with which science cannot deal—the nonanalytical, nonmeasurable, nonrepetitive part of life, within which intuition, feeling, and emotion play predominant roles, and within which the individual person asks, "Who am I?" . . . "What are my basic purposes?" . . . "What ought I do?" . . . "What is my duty?" . . . "What is the meaning of life?"

We have seen that the explanations of science, when traced down, disappear in either fog or assumption. The explanations of religion, on the other hand, are founded on faith and conviction. Of the two, the second basis seems to me the more satisfying.

Confirmation in science (even if shaky at its core, as Karl Popper has pointed out) has the attraction of being widespread. But it is by no means universal; the agreement is widespread only in the sense that the vote is preponderantly favorable within a small elite. Outside that elite, the individuals have no real grounds for agreement, and in fact couldn't care less. If you tot up all the persons who believe in electrons, accept evolution, understand DNA, and care about quasars, the number is negligible as compared with the number of individuals who believe in God.

Some scientists would undoubtedly counter by saying that the preceding paragraph is near-nonsense for the reason that the elite who really know about and believe in science do so on the grounds of *real evidence* (their emphasis), that everyone else believes in science indirectly but significantly because they see applied science and technology *work*, while (still in their view) there just isn't any "real evidence" of the necessity for or the value of religious convictions.

My answer to that is twofold. First, I side with the imagined critics in conceding—in proclaiming—that I too believe in science as a magnificently successful guide in producing, step after step, answers to the questions which science raises. However, I differ completely because I believe that science cannot raise a large proportion of the really significant questions, and believe that it will never be able to. And second, I assert that there is a vast body of evidence in the record of human experience that man needs convictions of a sort which science cannot furnish, and that religion can and does fill that need. The evidence in my own personal experience is fully as definite and convincing as the results of a laboratory experiment. When I must make a decision as to what I *ought* to do, my moral conscience furnishes me with instructions that are more explicit than the instructions an electron receives from the probability function ψ of quantum theory. Or as another case, when I go to church, I feel happier and better than when I do not. It is as simple as that.

Let us briefly take stock of the position in which we find ourselves, now that our century is more than two-thirds past.

On the one hand, man is confronted by a multitudinous diversity. Science has, with superb success, described a formidable array of detailed relationships, operating within a structure which reaches out to the farthest star and which probes to the interior of the nucleus and the gene. Art, music, poetry, religion—these all have their special insights, their realms of concern, their differing formulations. The practical world of affairs is fantastically complicated, confused, and puzzling. Life is so wildly multiple and so wildly various that it cannot be compressed into any one neat formulation. Life cannot be backed into a tight corner; no mind can challenge life to a single duel.

The artist, in his great wisdom, has never attempted

to do this. He has characteristically looked at small fragments of experience, but looked in such a way that he can see some aspect of the whole mirrored in the part.

Thinking, which is a chief tool used by science, deals competently with certain aspects of experience; but feeling, which often takes over where thinking leaves off, and which is a chief instrument for fashioning the rhythms, the patterns, and the illuminating symbolism of the arts, deals with quite other aspects of experience.

The philosopher has sometimes tried to construct unifying theories for the whole, but I am unaware of any attempt that has gained wide acceptance. One stubborn fact has always blocked such efforts. "Everyday experience confronts us with an inescapable duality: on the one hand, the tough resistant world of things, the complexities of which science is now untangling and reducing to the form of natural law; on the other hand ourselves, the thinkers, feelers, choosers, who do the measuring and ordering, and who seem to belong to a different realm of reality. . . . As Descartes pointed out long ago, we may systematically doubt everything, but the one undubitable fact is that something is doing the doubting." [7]

If it is true that we are steadily under the influence of centrifugal tendencies, which lead to more diversity and complexity, it is equally true that centripetal forces are at work, which keep pointing inward to central unities. This is evident in both the physical and the biological sciences. In the former, and despite the almost intolerable variety of the experimental evidence concerning the so-called elementary particles, we appear to be close to a theory which may simplify and unify all this complexity. As to the physical elements, we already have the main outlines of a theory that shows how they could all have evolved from a primitive simple beginning. In the realm of living matter, the unifying sweep of the Darwinian theory of evolution has been crowned by our knowledge of the DNA double helix, the beautiful molecular structure which both summarizes the past and provides for the future by storing genetic history and by possessing the capacity to replicate. Furthermore, this structure has been found to be the common central property of all forms of life, from the simplest single-celled creature to man. It is difficult to imagine any one fact of more impressive, and more unifying, significance.

In religion, historically so tortured by disagreeing factions, we now have ecumenical movements which make slow but promising progress. Even in the world-wide political scene, granting the staggering array of splintering disagreements, we do hold to the concept of an embracing organization. On a smaller, but still on a great scale, our own country is dedicated to the idea that unity can exist within diversity.

It is clear that in all aspects of our lives we have to deal with diversity and must continuously seek, within that variety, unifying features and principles. In my own youth I tolerated diversity primarily by not allowing the conflicting ideas to come to engagement. It was essentially true that I thought about religion on Sunday, about science in the working hours of weekdays, and about the humane arts in spare time.

I now firmly believe that that kind of compartmentalization is unsatisfactory. The paradoxes, the inconsistencies, the multiple contradictions have to be honestly faced; some of them have to be resolved, and some of them have to be accepted.

In the relationship between religion and science, I have for myself resolved essentially all of the conflicts by coming to believe in reasonable claims for each. Within science I have to accept certain deep inconsistencies (a wave *and* a particle) as I also do in religion (the emotional, personal God and the abstract, intellectual God).

These acceptances are formally justified in terms of the principle of complementarity; but they are made more agreeable by my realization that the dualities arise in large part from language and culture-bound limitations from which I cannot conceivably free myself and for which I need feel no responsibility.

I want to conclude by describing a sort of geometrical way of thinking about the relationships between the different realms of our experience and our concern. The geometrical metaphor arises from a useful trick that was introduced into complex variable theory by the great German mathematician Georg Friedrich Bernhard Riemann (1826–1866).

Several pages back we observed that the square root of a positive real number is a two-valued function, there always being two answers. This is an almost trivially simple case of what are called multiple-valued functions, and in the more sophisticated realm of what the mathematician calls "complex numbers" there can be really complicated situations when one deals with multiple-valued functions. To help in these situations Riemann introduced the idea of a multilayered surface, roughly like sheets of paper stacked on top of each other. The various layers of the multi-sheeted Riemann surface were cut along certain lines, and then two layers A and B could be interconnected by joining the right side of a cut on A to the left side of a cut on B, and similarly the left side of the cut on A to the right side of the cut on B. Using these crossover joins, a moving point on A could slide onto layer B, or vice versa.

I want you to think of a roughly similar geometrical situation, in which there is a considerable number of sheets in the layered stack, each of the sheets being as large as you please and so negligibly thin that if you concentrate attention on one, you can think of it as being right next to another one which interests you, no matter which this other one is. Each is next to all. That is a sort of Alice in Wonderland concept, but don't let it worry you.

Now each of our sheets is also cut along lines, as in the mathematical case, and not only are they criss-cross joined along these lines, permitting passage from the one sheet to the other, but a little stretching occurs along each cut so that they overlap on the criss-cross join, there being a band bordering the cut which is recognized to be a common part of both of the joined sheets.

I do hope this doesn't sound too complicated and fantastic! For in terms of these various sheets, each joined to every other one along a band which they share, I can describe my picture of the way our minds must deal with the multiplicity of the realms of our experience.

One of these sheets might be labeled "Science." On it there would be regions devoted to all the scientific specialties. These would all have "interior" portions (where topologists speak only to topologists, for example) and common portions (where physicists speak to astronomers, organic chemists to immunologists, and so on). There would be many cuts distributed around on this science sheet, where varying and intermingled viewpoints are criss-cross connected with the viewpoints of nonscientific activities. Thus mathematics shares a boundary strip along a cut which joins to music. The science sheet is cross-connected with a rather broad common band to the sheets devoted to the creative arts and to philosophy, and with a somewhat more narrow common band to the sheet devoted to religion.

All other fields have their sheets, similarly available for cross-connection. I suppose there is a cut and a common band shared between the natural sciences (what we have herein always meant by the word "science") and what are called the "social sciences"; but at the moment I would envisage that cut as not very extensive, and the band of shared area as being rather narrow and wrinkled.

A person's concerns can, at one moment, be located on one of the interior portions of a single sheet. This, for example, is the location occupied by the developmental embryologist when he is concentrating on an experiment in his laboratory. When he interprets this experiment, and when he thinks about its implications, he might wander broadly around over the science sheet. When he thinks about the developing embryo within his pregnant wife, he crosses over onto any one of numerous other sheets.

One cannot simultaneously occupy an interior position on two sheets—if he wishes to straddle two sets of concern, he moves to the shared band. He temporarily can, by staying inside his own sheet, compartmentalize his thinking—this often is the way he makes progress within his own field. But he should constantly remember that he also can, and sometimes must, occupy a position in which he is concerned with interconnections.

The whole stack of sheets, each with its own interior tapestry of intricate pattern, accommodates itself to the representation of a vast amount of complexity. The paradoxical fact that each sheet is next to every other sheet, that each sheet is, or can be, connected to any other sheet— that is an expression of the unity that pervades all the diversity. But the sheets are not glued tight together into one solid mass. As Oppenheimer said, "Occasionally between the sciences, and more rarely between a science and other parts of our experience and knowledge, there is a correspondence, or analogy, a partial mapping of two sets of ideas and words . . . *Everything can be related to anything; everything cannot be related to everything*" (my italics) .[8]

From a single interior position on one sheet, one can frame a question that receives, in this context, one answer. The same question, if framed within the context of another interior position on another sheet, may well receive a quite different—a contradictory—answer. Indeed, from two interior positions on the same sheet he may well receive two inconsistent but complementary answers.

The thinking of an individual is thus both compartmentalized and not compartmentalized. He shifts from a compartmentalized position on one sheet to a compartmentalized position on another sheet. He can carry out the process of shifting almost instantaneously—just stopping thinking about music and starting to think about supper— or he can pause as long as he likes in the common band shared by two sheets, spending a lifetime thinking about the relationships between science and religion.

I earnestly hope that no reader believes that I take this little geometrical fable too seriously. I do not. It does seem to me, however, to furnish a rather vivid way of thinking about the complexity and interrelatedness of our concerns.

Our hunches, intuitions, ideas, beliefs, and convictions are partly isolated and partly connected in an interlaced pattern that has portions blessed by consistency and other portions invigorated by contradiction.

The picture here presented does not have the specious tidiness of attempts at unitary viewpoints, but these ideas are supported by the realization that science recognizes that in its most fundamental theories, complementarity must be accepted. There is the comfort of knowing that logic has no power to prove the incorrectness of this viewpoint. It has the validity, the vigor, and the integrity of corresponding to the way life really is.

I believe that the ultimate unifying virtues are order, beauty, faith, and love. The emphasis of science decreases as one passes from the first to the last of these four words. The emphasis of religion, on the other hand, increases from first to fourth, culminating on the final one. The arts and the humanities primarily emphasize the central two. But the underlying unity being what it is, all are concerned with all.

As I write these closing lines I am for a time in residence at the Salk Institute of Biological Studies. There is here a most congenial atmosphere, for this organization is engaged in some of the most fundamental biological problems but is determined that these studies be carried out within the context of a wide concern for the utilization of this knowledge for the good of man. Most of the laboratory work here is at the molecular biological level, and I have just been rereading James D. Watson's marvelous account of the discovery of the structure of DNA.

This discovery of the detailed architecture of the

doubly helical molecule that is at the very focus of life is the kind of science that is as artistically beautiful as it is intellectually satisfying. There is presumably a considerable number of scientists (they are chiefly the young ones) who believe that all biological questions, ultimately including those about the behavior of man, will be answered in terms of physics and chemistry. These people are called reductionists. Among the reductionists are the extremists, of whom the British molecular biologist Francis Crick is the leader, who presumably believe[9] that the three-letter words coded on the DNA molecule* are capable of forming chemical sentences which provide the answers for any conceivable question that can be asked about how a living organism arises, develops, and functions.

Applauding the grand sweep of that idea, I dissent. I do not think molecular biology is going to be able to answer all of man's questions about himself. Francis Crick, of course, would hoot at this last sentence. He would doubtless point out that molecular biology will be able to answer all the well-posed and sensible questions, and that the other questions ought to be disregarded as trivial or meaningless. On his side would be a small group of very bright but some-

---

*The DNA molecule provides an alphabet of four letters (the four bases which form the stairsteps of the DNA helix). They store the information which can instruct the machinery of the cell what proteins to manufacture. The proteins are formed of long "sentences" made out of twenty "words" (the twenty amino acids). If you are lucky enough to have a young teen-ager in your house, he or she can explain to you that with four letters you can make sixteen two-letter words (which isn't enough to designate the amino acids, since there are twenty of them); whereas with these same four letters you can spell sixty-four three-letter words. This is more than enough, the surplus being used for synonyms, punctuation, and perhaps some non-sense syllables. Hence the genetic code is written out with the sixty-four three-letter words that can be made from four letters.

what acidulous young scientists. In the dissenting company are to be found the poets, the saints and the dreamers, the philosophers and the innocents, together with uncounted millions of humble, earnest, simple folk. Indeed, among this latter company, where I choose to be, are also many of the older thoughtful scientists. I could offer quoted testimony from many of them, but I will restrict myself to one example.

Vannevar Bush has been for many years one of the recognized leaders among the scientists of our country. He is a distinguished engineer, the energetic leader of the United States scientific effort in World War II. No one who has ever seen him bite into his pipe and crisply outline a course of practical action would ever think of calling him soft. In the chapter entitled "Threat and Bulwark" in his totally realistic book *Modern Arms and Free Men* Bush said, "Science has been misread. Science does not exclude faith. And faith alone can meet the threat that now hangs over us." [10] His most recent book, moreover, bears the title *Science Is Not Enough.*[11]

In this book the reader has found some very informal comments about myself and my activities, along with other portions which are as serious as I am capable of being. This shuffling up is not due to lazy organization along with an unwillingness to rewrite once again. It is deliberate. I am convinced that this is the way life is. Triviality and significance, gaiety and seriousness—these are complementary one to the other. I have always lived that sort of life, and for as much longer as is granted to me, I always will.

I will be seventy-five before this book is printed. At a number of times during its writing I was not at all confident that I would be around until it was finished. "I cannot tell," the French writer Maurice Goudeket wrote, "how I shall behave when aches and decrepitude come, or that illness which will thrust me, roughly or not so roughly, out of this world . . . I only beg that I may, without weakening, remain true to the oaths that I have inwardly sworn, honor the life dwelling within me to its very last; and even if only a spark remains to me, treat it still as a holy flame." [12]

REFERENCE NOTES
CHRONOLOGY
BIBLIOGRAPHY

Reference Notes

Chapter 3. Throop/Caltech

1. In connection with the history of Caltech, I have drawn from a series of three articles, "The Roots of the California Institute of Technology," written by Imra W. Buwalda, widow of John Peter Buwalda, chairman of Caltech's division of geology from 1925 to 1947, and published in *Engineering and Science*, October–December, 1966.

Chapter 5. The Rockefeller Foundation

1. Letter to the author dated 1931.
2. J. Cairns, G. S. Stent, J. D. Watson (eds.), *Phage and the Origins of Molecular Biology* (Cold Spring Harbor, N.Y.: Cold Spring Harbor Laboratory, 1966).
3. James D. Watson, *The Double Helix* (New York: Atheneum, 1968).
4. Letter to the author dated April 11, 1967.

Chapter 7. Postwar Activities

1. J. N. Efferson, *The Production and Marketing of Rice* (New Orleans: The Rice Journal, 1952).
2. "Revolution in Agriculture," *Nature*, August 10, 1968.
3. The memorandum I wrote forms the first chapter of the first

book written on this subject: William N. Locke and A. Donald Booth, *Machine Translation of Languages* (Cambridge, Mass.: M.I.T. Press, 1955); it also appears in Warren Weaver, *Science and Imagination* (New York: Basic Books, 1967).

4. Claude E. Shannon and Warren Weaver, *The Mathematical Theory of Communication* (Urbana, Ill.: University of Illinois Press, 1949).

Chapter 8. "Retirement"

1. Warren Weaver, *U.S. Philanthropic Foundations: Their History, Structure, Management, and Record* (New York: Harper & Row, 1967).

2. Warren Weaver, *Science and Imagination* (New York: Basic Books, 1967).

Chapter 9. Science Then and Now

1. E. B. Wilson, *The Cell in Development and Inheritance* (New York: Macmillan, 1896; reprinted by Johnson Reprint Corporation, New York, 1966).

Chapter 10. Some Limitations of Science

1. Alfred North Whitehead, *The Aims of Education* (New York: Macmillan, 1959).

2. James B. Conant, *Scientific Principles and Moral Conduct* (New York: Cambridge University Press, 1967).

3. Quoted in Theodore Morrison, "The Agitated Heart," *Atlantic Monthly*, July 1967, p. 79.

4. Karl Popper, *Logic of Scientific Discovery* (New York: Basic Books, 1959).

5. Thomas S. Kuhn, *The Structure of Scientific Revolutions* (Chicago: University of Chicago Press, 1962).

6. Benjamin Lee Whorf, *Language, Thought, and Reality* (Cambridge, Mass.: M.I.T. Press, 1956), particularly the chapter "Science and Linguistics." In addition to the direct quotations, many ideas expressed here are taken from this book.

7. Derek J. De Solla Price, "Joseph Needham and the Science of China," *Horizon*, Vol. X, No. 1 (Winter, 1968).

8. First introduced in an article by Max Planck in *Sitzungsberichte!* (Prussian Academy of Sciences, Berlin), 1889.

9. Geoffrey F. Chew, "The Dubious Role of the Space-Time Continuum in Microscopic Physics," *Science Progress*, Vol. LI, No. 204 (October 1963), p. 529.

10. Howard Nemerov, *The Blue Swallows* (Chicago: University of Chicago Press, 1968).

Chapter 11.   Science, Contradiction, and Religion

1. Leon Rosenfeld, "Niels Bohr in the Thirties," in S. Rozenthal, ed., *Niels Bohr* (New York: John Wiley & Sons, 1967).

2. Werner Heisenberg, "Quantum Theory and Its Interpretations," *ibid.*

3. J. Robert Oppenheimer, *The Open Mind* (New York: Simon & Schuster, 1955).

4. Quoted in *Saturday Review*, September 30, 1967, p. 31.

5. Quoted in *Saturday Review*, *loc. cit.*

6. Leo Tolstoy, *Life and Essays on Religion,* translated by Alylmer Maude (World Classics, Oxford: Oxford University Press, 1934).

7. From a review of Suzanne K. Langer, *Mind: An Essay on Human Feeling,* Vol. 1 (Baltimore: Johns Hopkins Press, 1967) by Robert MacCleod, *Science,* September 29, 1967.

8. In his address, "Science and Our Times," delivered at the Roosevelt University Founders and Friends Dinner, Chicago, May 22, 1956.

9. See Francis Crick, *Of Molecules and Men* (Seattle: University of Washington Press, 1967).

10. Vannevar Bush, *Modern Arms and Free Men* (New York: Simon and Schuster, 1949).

11. Vannevar Bush, *Science Is Not Enough* (New York: Morrow, 1967).

12. Maurice Goudeket, *The Delights of Growing Old* (New York: Farrar, Straus & Giroux, 1966).

Chronology

1894   Born July 17, Reedsburg, Wisconsin, son of Isaiah and Kittie Belle (Stupfell) Weaver.

1912   Graduated from Central High School, Madison, Wisconsin.

1916   B.S. in Civil Engineering, University of Wisconsin.

1917   C.E., University of Wisconsin.

1917–18   Assistant professor of mathematics, Throop College, Pasadena, California.

1918–19   Second lieutenant, Air Service, United States Army.

1919   Married Mary Hemenway, September 1, at Carlsbad, New Mexico.

1919–20   Assistant professor of mathematics, California Institute of Technology.

1920–32   Department of mathematics, University of Wisconsin: assistant professor, 1920–25; associate professor, 1925–28; professor and chairman of department, 1928–32.

209

1932–52 Director, Division of Natural Sciences, Rockefeller Foundation.

1940–42 Chairman, Fire Control Section, Office of Scientific Research and Development.

1941 War mission in England.

1943–46 Chief, Applied Mathematics Panel, OSRD.

1945 First Chairman, Naval Research Advisory Committee.

1946–47 Member, War Department Research Advisory Panel.

1948 British Medal for Service in the Cause of Freedom.
Medal for Merit of the United States.
Honorary degree of Doctor of Law, University of Wisconsin, the first of a number of honorary degrees.

1950 Officer of the Legion of Honor of France.

1952 President, American Association for the Advancement of Science.

1952–53 Chairman, Basic Research Group, Research and Development Board, U.S. Department of Defense.

1952–59 Vice president for Natural and Medical Sciences, The Rockefeller Foundation.

1955–59 Chairman, Committee on Scientific Policy, Sloan Kettering Institute for Cancer Research.

1956–67 Trustee, Alfred P. Sloan Foundation.

1957   Public Welfare Medal, National Academy of Sciences.

1958   Fellow, American Academy of Arts and Sciences.

1959   Retired from The Rockefeller Foundation.

1960–67 Vice chairman of board, and chairman, committee on scientific policy, Memorial Sloan Kettering Cancer Center.

1961   Member, governing council, Courant Institute of Mathematics, New York University, New York City. Trustee, Salk Institute for Biological Studies.

1962   Chairman, board of trustees, and non-resident fellow, Salk Institute.

1965   Dedication of Warren Weaver Hall, New York University, New York City.
        Kalinga Prize, awarded for literary excellence in scientific writing by international committee set up by UNESCO.
        Arches of Science Award, Pacific Science Center.

1967   Medallion Medal of the Sloan Kettering Memorial Cancer Center.

1969   Elected to National Academy of Sciences.

Selected Bibliography

The Electromagnetic Field. By Max Mason and Warren
Weaver. Chicago: University of Chicago Press, 1929; pa-
perback ed., New York: Dover, 1946.
An advanced text for graduate students.

The Scientists Speak. Edited, and with a general introduction
and chapter introductions, by Warren Weaver. New York:
Boni and Gaer, Inc., 1947.
Brief expositions of eighty-one scientific topics by well-
known scientists, written for the general reader.

The Mathematical Theory of Communication. By Claude E.
Shannon and Warren Weaver. Urbana, Ill.: University of
Illinois Press, 1949; paperback ed., 1964.
A technical and mathematical presentation of the theory,
followed by an exposition accessible to the general
reader.

Lady Luck. Garden City, N.Y.: Doubleday & Company, Inc.,
1963.
A popular exposition of the theory of probability and
its applications; translated into Danish, German, He-
brew, Polish, Rumanian, Spanish, Swedish, and Japanese.

Alice in Many Tongues. Madison, Wis.: The University of Wisconsin Press, 1964.

> An account of the writing of *Alice in Wonderland and* its translations into approximately 50 languages, with a checklist of the translations.

U.S. Philanthropic Foundations—Their History, Structure, Management, and Record. New York: Harper and Row, 1967.

Science and Imagination. New York: Basic Books, 1967.

> A collection of essays on science, science and the citizen, science and religion, and a number of other subjects, including Lewis Carroll.

INDEX

INDEX

Thomas, Dylan, 182
Thomas, Franklin, 42
Thompson, Lawrance, 47
Thomson, Joseph J., 144
Throop, Amos G., 39
Throop College, 36 ff
time, concept of, 163, 166, 167, 168, 171
Town & Gown, 52
Toynbee, Arnold, 162
transportation and communication, 136–138, 141
Trollope, Anthony, 53
Turner, Frederick J., 52
Tuve, Merle, 84

ultraviolet light, 61
uranium 235, energy of, 138

Van Hise, Charles R., 52
Van Vleck, Edward B., 49–50
Veblen, Oswald, 87
von Frisch, Karl, 67
von Seysenegg, Erich T., 151

Wallace, Henry A., 94
Wallis, W. Allen, 88
Warburg, Otto, 60
Warren Weaver Hall, 113
Watson, Ernest, 47
Watson, James, 72, 73, 198–199
wave mechanics, 56
Weaver, Cicely Ann Kavanaugh (stepmother), 19, 20, 53
Weaver, Helen (daughter), 53
Weaver, Isaiah (father), 1, 6, 15, 18, 19, 20–21, 52, 209

Weaver, Kittie Belle Stupfell (mother), 8, 15
Weaver, Mary Hemenway, *see* Hemenway, Mary
Weaver, Paul John (brother), 11, 12, 21
Weaver, Warren
   and Academy of Religion and Mental Health, 115–116
   acrobatic flying, 45
   and American Association for the Advancement of Science, 116–117
   ancestors, 5–8
   birthdays, 10–11
   childhood, 7–8, 11–12
   Chronology, 209–211
   college, 24
   early years, 1 ff
   in England, 90–93
   European travel, 66, 76
   in the Far East, 100
   foreign tours, 68–69
   Fourth of July, 9–10
   friendships, 15–16
   and Health Research Council of New York City, 115
   and India, 100
   marriage, 34, 45–47
   May Day pleasures, 5
   and National Science Foundation, 113–114
   and Naval Research Advisory Committee, 113
   New York, first days in, 63
   in Paris, 64
   reading adventures, 17
   retirement, 117 ff
   and Rockefeller Foundation, 59 ff, 117–118

Weaver, Warren *(cont.)*
    and Salk Institute, 128, 129
    schooldays, 16
    schoolteachers, 19, 21–23
    student plays, 23
    Tau Beta Pi membership, 34
    teaching experiences, 33, 49 ff, 58
    violin playing, 13–14
    and War Department Research, 113
    war years, 76 ff
Weaver, Warren, Jr., 53
Wentzel, Gregor, 56

wheat, 100
Wheeler, John A., 169, 173
Whitehead, A. N., 154
Whorf, Benjamin Lee, 162, 164, 165, 178
Wiener, Norbert, 106
Wilks, Samuel S., 87
Wilson, Carroll, 89
Wilson, Edmund Beecher, 151
Wilson, Woodrow, 76
Wolfle, Dael, 117

X ray, 61, 144
X-ray diffraction methods, 71, 75